McGraw-Hill

networks™

A Social Studies Learning System

Sociology & You

CHAPTER TESTS AND LESSON QUIZZES

McGraw Hill Education

Bothell, WA • Chicago, IL • Columbus, OH • New York, NY

Cover Image Credit: Blind Feeling, 1996, Giclee Print by artist Diana Ong, Diana Ong/SuperStock/Getty Images.

www.mheonline.com/networks

McGraw Hill Education

Send all inquiries to:
McGraw-Hill Education
8787 Orion Place
Columbus, OH 43240

ISBN: 978-0-07-664069-0
MHID: 0-07-664069-8

Printed in the United States of America.

4 5 6 7 8 9 QVS 20 19 18 17 16

The McGraw·Hill Companies

Table of Contents

Chapter 6 Groups and Formal Organizations

Chapter 7 Deviance and Social Control

Chapter 8 Social Stratification

Chapter 9 Inequalities of Race and Ethnicity

Chapter 10 Inequalities of Gender and Age

Chapter 11 The Family

Chapter 12 Education

Chapter 13 Political and Economic Institutions

Chapter 14 Religion

Chapter 15 Population and Urbanization

Chapter 16 Social Change and Collective Behavior

NAME ______________________ DATE ______________ CLASS __________

Lesson Quiz 1-1

networks

An Invitation to Sociology

DIRECTIONS: True/False In the blank, indicate whether the statement is true (T) or false (F).

_______ **1.** Psychologists study the behavior of individuals.

_______ **2.** The sociological perspective only studies an individual's behavior.

_______ **3.** Anthropologists focus mainly on modern, industrial societies.

_______ **4.** Individuals do not change their behavior to match the expectations of a group.

_______ **5.** One way to develop the sociological imagination is to look at your own society as an outsider.

DIRECTIONS: Multiple Choice Indicate the answer choice that best completes the statement or answers the question.

_______ **6.** Which of the following best describes the sociological perspective?

A. Its major focus is on individual differences.
B. Its major focus is the intelligence of individuals.
C. It focuses on people at a group level.
D. It has little interest in group behavior.

_______ **7.** What is one way that sociology and history differ?

A. Sociologists use a wider range of research methods.
B. Only historians use historical documents and oral histories.
C. Historians focus mainly on observation and interviews.
D. Only sociologists interpret the evidence they gather.

_______ **8.** Which of the following is part of the unique perspective of sociology?

A. the behavior of individuals in isolation
B. patterns of behavior in social relationships
C. the mental and emotional processes of individuals
D. the history and theory of government

_______ **9.** Which of the following is a characteristic of groups?

A. Groups have the same characteristics as the people who form them.
B. They encourage individuals to behave independently.
C. Every group is only a collection of individuals.
D. They are separate from the individuals who form them.

_______ **10.** What is the sociological imagination?

A. A method sociologists use to uncover new sources of information.
B. The ability of individuals to adapt to the expectations of a group.
C. The way individuals see how events in their own lives relate to events in society.
D. A creative way for sociologists to represent social processes.

NAME ____________________ DATE ____________________ CLASS ____________

Lesson Quiz 1-2

networks

An Invitation to Sociology

DIRECTIONS: Matching Match each item with the correct statement below.

______ **1.** stressed that people behave based on their own understanding of a situation		**A.** W.E.B. Du Bois
		B. Émile Durkheim
______ **2.** writer who believed that there is conflict between the bourgeoisie and the proletariat		**C.** Karl Marx
______ **3.** social reformer and co-founder of Chicago's Hull House		**D.** Max Weber
______ **4.** social activist who was involved in the Pan-African movement		**E.** Jane Addams
______ **5.** sociologist who stressed the importance of consensus in a society		

DIRECTIONS: Multiple Choice Indicate the answer choice that best completes the statement or answers the question.

______ **6.** Karl Marx believed that class conflict was inevitable because

A. latent functions are more common than manifest functions.

B. social interdependence always leads to social unrest.

C. Social Darwinism states that a classless society is the most stable type of society.

D. workers will eventually overthrow capitalists just as enslaved persons overthrew their owners.

______ **7.** Jane Addams

A. was concerned about the exploitation of the lower class.

B. believed everyone should find his or her social-class level without outside interference.

C. was the first person to research the social structure of African American communities.

D. is considered the founder of symbolic interactionism.

______ **8.** The theory that society benefits when each individual finds his or her own social-class level without outside interference is called

A. group conformity. **C.** group imagination.

B. class conflict. **D.** Social Darwinism.

______ **9.** Harriet Martineau is considered an early feminist theorist because she

A. thought that conflict between the proletariat and the bourgeoisie was inevitable.

B. wrote about the link between slavery and the oppression of women.

C. campaigned for equal pay for women.

D. believed women were free to find their own social-class level.

______ **10.** Who was the social worker who studied the lives of people along the Mexican-American border?

A. Charles Darwin **C.** George Herbert Mead

B. Jane Addams **D.** Julian Samora

NAME ______________________ DATE ______________ CLASS ______________

Lesson Quiz 1-3

networks

An Invitation to Sociology

DIRECTIONS: Modified True/False In the blank, indicate whether the statement is true (T) or false (F). If false edit the statement to make it a true statement.

_______ **1.** A manifest function is unintended and unrecognized.

____

_______ **2.** Symbolic interactionism focuses on mutually understood symbols.

____

_______ **3.** Supporters of the conflict perspective see social living as a contest for resources.

____

_______ **4.** Social structure refers to the occasional patterns of social behaviors in a group or society.

____

_______ **5.** Functionalism assumes that societies will not return to a state of stability after periods of upheaval.

____

DIRECTIONS: Multiple Choice Indicate the answer choice that best completes the statement or answers the question.

_______ **6.** What do sociologists mean by theoretical perspective?

A. facts and data about society
B. opinions about how people should relate
C. consensus among all members of a group
D. assumptions about the workings of society

_______ **7.** The distribution of power is most important in which of the following theoretical perspectives?

A. symbolic interactionism
B. functionalism
C. the conflict perspective
D. positivism

_______ **8.** Which of the following emphasizes the contributions of each part of society and how these parts work together to create a unified whole?

A. symbolic interactionism
B. the conflict perspective
C. functionalism
D. positivism

_______ **9.** Which theoretical perspective shows that people can communicate because they share words, gestures, and physical objects that have similar meanings to all of them?

A. symbolic interactionism
B. the conflict perspective
C. functionalism
D. positivism

_______ **10.** According to Émile Durkheim, where is consensus strongest?

A. in small tribal societies
B. in large industrial societies
C. in universities
D. in countries with large international trade

Chapter 1 Test, Form A

networks

An Invitation to Sociology

DIRECTIONS: Matching Match each item with the correct statement below.

______ **1.** the definition of sociology	**A.** unintended and unrecognized consequences of an aspect of society
______ **2.** Auguste Comte	**B.** advocated the scientific study of society
______ **3.** *verstehen*	**C.** interdependence of parts in a system
______ **4.** functional integration	**D.** scientific study of social structure
______ **5.** latent functions	**E.** understanding social behavior by putting yourself in the place of others
______ **6.** sociological imagination	**F.** set of assumptions about an area of study
______ **7.** rationalization	**G.** intended and recognized consequences of an aspect of society
______ **8.** symbolic interactionism	**H.** ability to see the link between society and self
______ **9.** theoretical perspective	**I.** mind-set that uses knowledge, reason, and planning
______ **10.** manifest functions	**J.** focuses on the interaction among people

DIRECTIONS: Multiple Choice Indicate the answer choice that best completes the statement or answers the question.

______ **11.** Several members of a little league team begin wearing their baseball caps backward and soon the entire team is following this style. This is an example of

A. social structure.

B. group conformity.

C. group imagination.

D. Social Darwinism.

______ **12.** The changes caused by the Industrial Revolution, such as people moving from farms to cities, is an example of social

A. conformity.

B. Darwinism.

C. dynamics.

D. relativism.

Chapter 1 Test, Form A *cont.*

An Invitation to Sociology

_______ **13.** Shopping on the Internet is convenient, and can save time. This is a __________ function of this type of shopping.

A. latent

B. dynamic

C. static

D. manifest

_______ **14.** When an athlete holds a clenched fist over her head after scoring a point, she is using a

A. function.

B. symbol.

C. *verstehen*.

D. rationalization.

_______ **15.** What is an important difference between sociology and anthropology?

A. Sociology studies human mental processes; anthropology deals with human emotions.

B. Anthropology studies social structure; sociology studies culture.

C. Sociology studies the theory of government; anthropology studies how government works.

D. Sociology investigates social behavior from a group perspective; anthropology investigates culture.

_______ **16.** What did Harriet Martineau see a link between?

A. slavery and the oppression of women

B. the proletariat and the bourgeoisie

C. Social Darwinism and the advancement of women

D. educational opportunity and social structure

_______ **17.** Using e-mail has decreased the number of hand-written letters that people send to their friends and relatives. This is a __________ function of e-mail.

A. static

B. dynamic

C. latent

D. manifest

_______ **18.** __________ emphasize that people can communicate because they share words, gestures, and physical objects that have similar meanings to all of them.

A. Symbolic interactionists

B. Functionalists

C. Conflict theorists

D. Positivists

______ **19.** Your mother believes that you should cook the family dinner every Wednesday night because it is part of your family duties. You believe you should not have to cook because it takes too long and cuts into after-school activities. You and your mother have different

A. symbols.

B. structures.

C. perspectives.

D. social dynamics.

______ **20.** Although there is no requirement concerning attire for the high school tennis team, the members all wear white clothing to competitions. This is an example of group

A. social statics.

B. perspective.

C. positivism.

D. conformity.

DIRECTIONS: Essay Answer the following questions on a separate sheet of paper.

21. Write a letter to the principal or guidance counselor at your cousin's school stating why implementing a sociology class would benefit both the students and the community. Persuade the principal to include this new course in next term's course offerings.

> "To be a poor man is hard, but to be a poor race in a land of dollars is the very bottom of hardships."
>
> —W.E.B. Du Bois, from *The Souls of Black Folk*, 1903

22. What do you think this quote from W.E.B. Du Bois means? Is it still relevant today? How do you think a psychologist would view this quote? How would a sociologist view this quote?

NAME ______________________ DATE ______________ CLASS __________

Chapter 1 Test, Form B

networks

An Invitation to Sociology

DIRECTIONS: Matching Match each item with the correct statement below.

______ **1.** conflict perspective

______ **2.** social statics

______ **3.** conformity

______ **4.** C. Wright Mills

______ **5.** dysfunction

______ **6.** rationalization

______ **7.** Karl Marx

______ **8.** anthropology

______ **9.** functionalism

______ **10.** power

A. a sociologist who coined the term sociological imagination

B. emphasizes the contributions of each part of a society

C. negative consequences of an aspect of society

D. social stability and order

E. emphasizes competition and constraint

F. hoped to form a classless society

G. a key influence in the change from a preindustrial to an industrial society

H. behavior that matches group expectations

I. social science that studies culture

J. ability to control the behavior of others

DIRECTIONS: Multiple Choice Indicate the answer choice that best completes the statement or answers the question.

______ **11.** Some people think that shopping over the Internet can lead to social isolation because people go to stores less frequently. This is a ________ function of Internet shopping.

A. latent

B. dynamic

C. static

D. manifest

______ **12.** When a baby waves "bye-bye," he is using a

A. function.

B. symbol.

C. *verstehen.*

D. rationalization.

______ **13.** When government regulations become so complex that they make it hard for citizens to accomplish their work efficiently, the negative result is

A. proletarianism.

B. dynamics.

C. dysfunction.

D. solidarity.

_______ **14.** According to _______, the people with the most power are seen as the most valuable to society.

A. symbolic interactionism

B. functionalism

C. conflict theory

D. positivism

_______ **15.** Which of the following is true of organic solidarity?

A. It existed in preindustrial times.

B. Most people have highly specialized roles.

C. There is a widespread consensus of values.

D. There is little interdependence among people.

_______ **16.** Which of the following best describes the sociological perspective?

A. a focus on patterns of behavior among members of a group

B. the study of the production and consumption of goods

C. the synthesis and interpretation of historical evidence

D. a focus on the development and functioning of the individual

_______ **17.** Which sociological perspective is associated with George Herbert Mead?

A. functionalism

B. positivism

C. the sociological imagination

D. symbolic interactionism

_______ **18.** What does the sociological imagination help us appreciate?

A. the psychology of dreams

B. the pioneers of sociology

C. cultural differences

D. the advantages of a classless society

_______ **19.** Which key concept of sociology emphasizes language, norms, values, and beliefs?

A. social action

B. integration

C. power

D. culture

_______ **20.** What did W.E.B. Du Bois criticize?

A. class based social structure

B. the assumption that African Americans are inferior

C. the move from agricultural to industrial society

D. the belief in Social Darwinism

Chapter 1 Test, Form B *cont.*

An Invitation to Sociology

DIRECTIONS: Essay Answer the following questions on a separate sheet of paper.

> "There are Bohemians, Italians, Poles, Russians, Greeks, and Arabs in Chicago vainly trying to adjust their peasant life to the life of a large city and coming in contact with only the most ignorant Americans in that city. The more of scholarship, the more of linguistic attainment, the more of beautiful surroundings a Settlement among them can command, the more it can do for them.
>
> Perhaps of more value than to the newly arrived peasant is the service of the Settlement to those foreigners who speak English fairly well, and who have been so successful in material affairs that they are totally absorbed by them."
>
> —Jane Addams, from "The Objective Value of a Social Settlement," (1893)

21. Read this passage from an essay written by Jane Addams, a pioneer American sociologist. She writes of the customs of various European peoples in their home countries. What does she suggest about what will happen to these immigrants after they have lived in the United States for a while? Do you think she would be as accurate in describing what would happen to immigrants who come to the United States today?

22. Important changes have occurred in the development of sociology in the United States since 1900. Choose one American sociologist who has made a contribution to sociology, and explain the reasons for this choice.

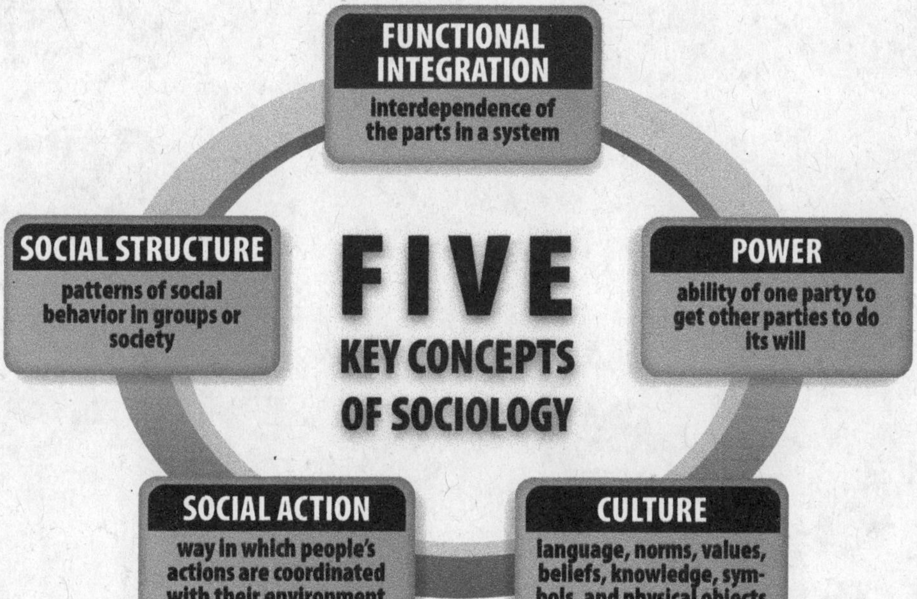
FUNCTIONAL INTEGRATION
interdependence of the parts in a system
SOCIAL STRUCTURE
patterns of social behavior in groups or society
FIVE
KEY CONCEPTS OF SOCIOLOGY
POWER
ability of one party to get other parties to do its will
SOCIAL ACTION
way in which people's actions are coordinated with their environment
CULTURE
language, norms, values, beliefs, knowledge, symbols, and physical objects shared by a group or society

23. This illustration shows the key concepts of sociology. What can you infer from the fact that the concepts are shown in a circle? What do you think it might mean if the key concepts were arranged in a straight line? What might it mean if the key concepts were arranged as a pyramid?

NAME ________________________ DATE ______________ CLASS __________

Lesson Quiz 2-1

networks

Sociological Research Methods

DIRECTIONS: Matching Match each item with the correct statement below.

_______ **1.** all people with the characteristics a researcher wants to study

_______ **2.** a trained person asks the questions and records the answers during this process

_______ **3.** a written set of questions that participants answer

_______ **4.** research method in which people respond to questions

_______ **5.** a limited number of cases drawn from the larger population

A. questionnaire

B. sample

C. interview

D. population

E. survey

DIRECTIONS: Multiple Choice Indicate the answer choice that best completes the statement or answers the question.

_______ **6.** What is one advantage of a closed-ended question survey?

A. Responses are limited to pre-set answers.

B. Surveys can be expensive to produce.

C. Many people do not respond to surveys.

D. A large number of responses can be collected.

_______ **7.** Which of the following is most closely associated with qualitative research?

A. surveys

B. participant observation

C. pre-collected data

D. numerical analysis

_______ **8.** Which research method would a functionalist most likely choose?

A. interview

B. participant observation

C. survey

D. case study

_______ **9.** Which of the following is a term used to describe secondary analysis?

A. reviewing survey research

B. graphing data visually

C. reviewing experimental research

D. using precollected data

_______ **10.** What is one advantage of using graphs and tables?

A. They enable people to see trends and relationships quickly.

B. They use colorful visual materials to present data.

C. They allow participants to respond in their own words.

D. They give wider access to new information.

NAME ________________ DATE ________________ CLASS ________________

Lesson Quiz 2-2

networks

Sociological Research Methods

DIRECTIONS: True/False In the blank, indicate whether the statement is true (T) or false (F).

________ **1.** Examples of variables include marital status, country of residence, race, education, and favorite foods.

________ **2.** Most of the events that occur in our lives have only one cause.

________ **3.** Research methods can be divided into two categories: quantitative and qualitative.

________ **4.** Causation is the belief that events occur in random, unpredictable ways.

________ **5.** To determine a causal relationship all other potential causal factors considered and recognized and included or eliminated.

DIRECTIONS: Multiple Choice Indicate the answer choice that best completes the statement or answers the question.

________ **6.** Research can be divided into two broad categories:

A. surveys and questionnaires.
B. quantitative and qualitative.
C. populations and samples.
D. case studies and interviews.

________ **7.** Assume that a researcher has determined that the more hours a student works at a job, the lower his grades in school will be. This is an example of a

A. false hypothesis.
B. positive correlation.
C. negative correlation.
D. secondary analysis.

________ **8.** Which of the following is true concerning causation?

A. Causation always exists if two variables are correlated.
B. Most events have a single cause.
C. Most events have multiple causes.
D. The concept of causation states that events occur in unpredictable, random ways.

________ **9.** Which of the following is a standard for showing causation?

A. The dependent variable changes before the independent variable changes.
B. Two variables are not correlated.
C. Only one factor must be taken into account.
D. Empirical evidence must be collected.

________ **10.** Which of the following is an example of a spurious correlation?

A. Rising poverty rates correlate to rising crime rates.
B. People with long arms also have long legs.
C. Eating a balanced diet keeps you healthy.
D. Studying more usually leads to better grades.

Lesson Quiz 2-3

Sociological Research Methods

DIRECTIONS: True/False In the blank, indicate whether the statement is true (T) or false (F).

_______ **1.** When conducting research, sociologists must always consider the ethical implications of their research methods.

_______ **2.** The scientific method involves the pursuit of knowledge in a non-systematic way.

_______ **3.** One example of an unethical experiment was the refusal to treat African Americans with syphilis so that the long-term effects of their disease could be studied.

_______ **4.** The knowledge gained from scientific experiments is more important than protecting the rights of research subjects.

_______ **5.** One of the important early steps in the research process is to review the literature.

DIRECTIONS: Multiple Choice Indicate the answer choice that best completes the statement or answers the question.

_______ **6.** You want to conduct research on the importance of practicing algebra problems daily and the grades earned in this subject. You write down in you notebook: *Students who work out practice problems daily will get a higher grade in algebra.* This is

A. a spurious correlation.
B. impossible to test.
C. a hypothesis.
D. an analysis of the results of the research..

_______ **7.** Which of the following is the last step in the research process?

A. analyze data
B. state findings and conclusions
C. identify the problem
D. collect data

_______ **8.** Which of the following is a standard for conducting ethical research?

A. Researchers can limit their objectivity if the study is important.
B. Researchers can ignore data that does not support their hypothesis.
C. Researchers can ignore their bias when doing research.
D. Researchers can identify research subjects only with the subject's consent.

_______ **9.** Why do some people regard the Stanford Prison Experiment as unethical?

A. Subjects were put in stressful situations without being told the true nature of the experiment.
B. Researchers failed to disclose the identity of the research subjects.
C. Findings and methods were not reported truthfully to the public.
D. The study did not follow professional standards of objectivity.

_______ **10.** Why is the scientific method used when conducting scientific research?

A. It encourages randomness when doing research.
B. It enhances social responsibility.
C. It lessens the need for professional competence.
D. It provides a systematic way to pursue knowledge.

NAME ____________________ DATE ____________ CLASS ____________

Chapter 2 Test, Form A

networks

Sociological Research Methods

DIRECTIONS: Matching Match each item with the correct item below.

_______ **1.** qualitative variable

_______ **2.** secondary analysis

_______ **3.** the concept of multiple causation

_______ **4.** research sample

_______ **5.** hypothesis

_______ **6.** population

_______ **7.** correlation

_______ **8.** case study

_______ **9.** scientific method

_______ **10.** plagiarism

A. using pre-collected information

B. an event that occurs as a result of several factors working in combination

C. focus on a single group, incident, or community

D. defined by membership in a category

E. a statement of relationships among well-defined variables

F. a group of people who represent a larger population

G. research that involves the pursuit of knowledge in a systematic way

H. the stealing of someone else's work

I. the people a researcher wants to study

J. a measure of how things are related to one another

DIRECTIONS: Multiple Choice Indicate the answer choice that best completes the statement or answers the question.

_______ **11.** A researcher sends you a form to fill out concerning your favorite movies. This is an example of

A. a questionnaire.

B. a sample.

C. secondary analysis.

D. multiple causation.

_______ **12.** An interviewer asks you to name your three favorite ways to spend your leisure time. This is an example of a (an) _______ question.

A. correlation

B. representative

C. closed-ended

D. open-ended

_______ **13.** What happens in a negative correlation?

A. The variables do not change.

B. The variables change in opposite directions.

C. The variables change in the same direction.

D. Only the independent variables change.

______ **14.** You want to conduct research on the importance of teenagers taking driver's education. Before you begin collecting data, you write down the following: *Teenagers who have taken driver's education will have fewer accidents in their first two years of driving than teenagers who have not taken driver's education.* What would the dependent variable be?

A. being a teenager

B. taking driver's education

C. the age of the teenager

D. the number of accidents a driver had

______ **15.** Which research method would be most useful in symbolic interactionism?

A. participant observation

B. survey

C. experiment

D. case study

______ **16.** A researcher is interested in studying the behavior of high-school basketball teams. Over one season, she joins the team during practice, watching the players' interactions first-hand. What type of research is this?

A. a questionnaire

B. an interview

C. a case study

D. participant observation

______ **17.** Which of the following is an example of unethical research?

A. Research subjects agreeing to try untested products after they are told of possible dangers.

B. Students participating in a psychological study after signing a confidentiality agreement.

C. Medical experiments conducted on prisoners who are not informed of potential side effects.

D. Surveys conducted in low-income neighborhoods with a guarantee of confidentiality.

______ **18.** Which of the following questions best helps you evaluate information on the Internet?

A. What is the quantity of information?

B. How many people have visited the site?

C. Where did the information come from?

D. Does the site use graphics effectively?

______ **19.** The final step when conducting research is to

A. analyze the data.

B. develop a hypothesis.

C. collect the data.

D. state findings and conclusions.

______ **20.** Which of the following is the number that divides a series of values in half?

A. mean

B. mode

C. average

D. median

DIRECTIONS: Essay Answer each of the following questions.

21. If a case study involves participant observation, what ethical issues should be considered prior to beginning the research?

____

____

____

____

____

____

____

____

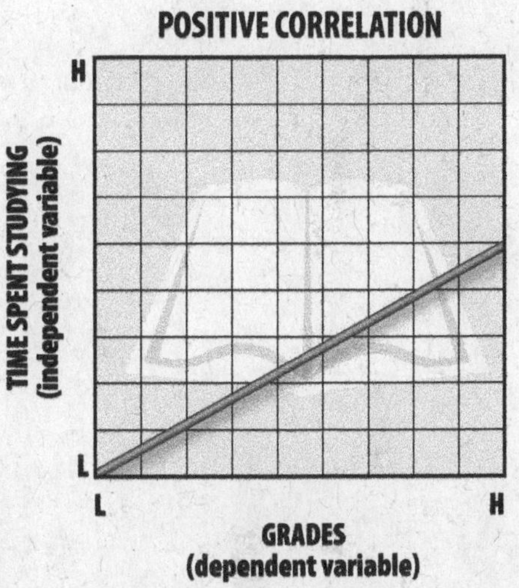

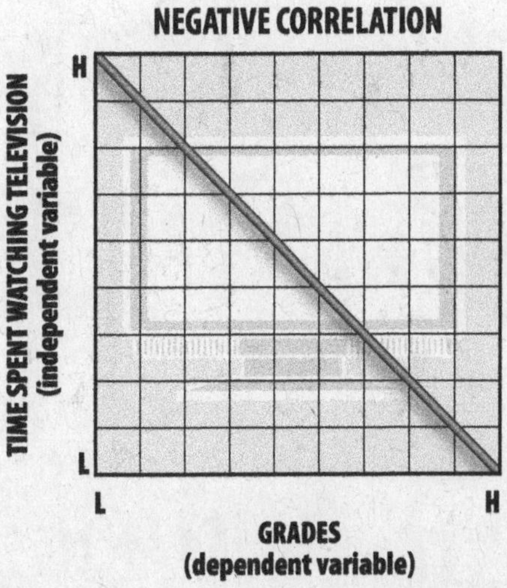

22. Look at the two graphs. One shows a positive correlation, the other shows a negative correlation. Explain the difference between these two types of correlations. Then describe in words what each graph shows. Finally, on a separate piece of paper, create a new graph that shows that studying for a certain amount of time improved your grade, while studying for a longer time period actually decreased your grade in sociology.

____

____

____

____

____

Sociological Research Methods

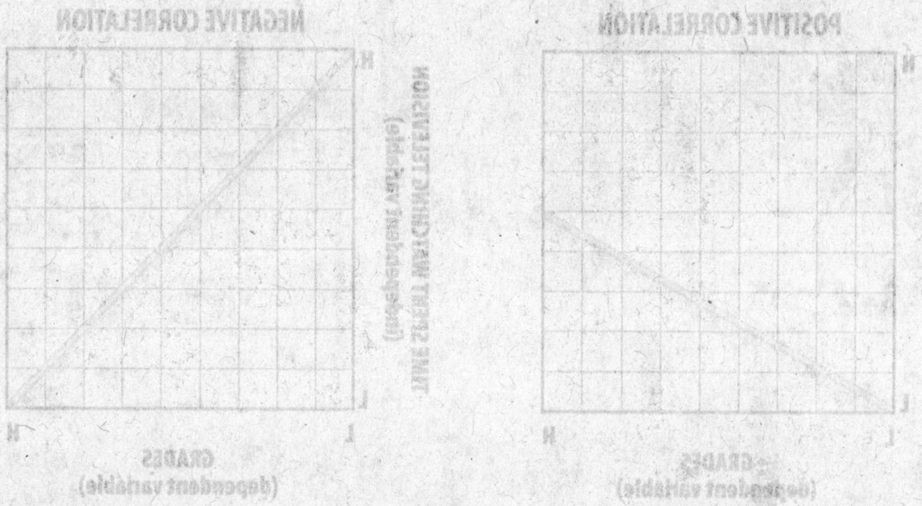

NAME ______________________ DATE ______________ CLASS __________

Chapter 2 Test, Form B

networks

Sociological Research Methods

DIRECTIONS: Matching Match each item with the correct item below.

_______ **1.** scientific method

_______ **2.** spurious correlation

_______ **3.** demographics

_______ **4.** graphs and tables

_______ **5.** causation

_______ **6.** ethics

_______ **7.** mode

_______ **8.** variable

_______ **9.** mean

_______ **10.** open-ended question

A. the number that occurs most frequently

B. a relationship caused by a third factor

C. allow people to quickly see trends in data

D. the belief that events occur in predictable ways and that one event leads to another

E. statistics that describe the characteristics of a population

F. research method that involves the pursuit of knowledge in a systematic way

G. a person's responses are in his or her own words

H. the number that lies somewhere in the middle of a range of numbers

I. a characteristic that is subject to change

J. rules that distinguish acceptable conduct

DIRECTIONS: Multiple Choice Indicate the answer choice that best completes the statement or answers the question.

_______ **11.** A questionnaire asks you to indicate your average marks in the science courses you completed in high school. Your answer is an example of a _______ variable.

A. correlative

B. quantitative

C. qualitative

D. causative

_______ **12.** Which research method would a conflict theorist most likely choose?

A. survey

B. interview

C. case study

D. participant observation

_______ **13.** Which of the following is an example of a positive correlation?

A. Grades improve as study time increases.

B. Grades remain the same as study time increases.

C. Grades go down as study time goes up.

D. Grades go up as study time decreases.

Chapter 2 Test, Form B *cont.*

networks

Sociological Research Methods

_______ **14.** What is one advantage of secondary analysis?

A. inexpensive

B. use of statistical techniques

C. laboratory environments artificial

D. information can be used by other researchers for a different purpose

_______ **15.** The first step in the research process is to

A. analyze the data.

B. identify the problem.

C. develop a hypothesis.

D. state findings and conclusions.

_______ **16.** Which of the following best describes field research?

A. Research that takes place in a natural setting.

B. Research that is conducted in a laboratory.

C. Information that is gathered by survey.

D. Information that is measured quantitatively.

_______ **17.** Which of the following is a historical example of an unethical experiment?

A. using corpses in automobile crash tests

B. testing cosmetic products on willing participants

C. conducting autopsies on corpses

D. studying the cause of cancer in tissue samples from patients

_______ **18.** Which of the following best describes an average?

A. A number that represents the lowest figure in a set.

B. A number that represents the highest figure in a set.

C. A number that represents the distribution of several figures.

D. The combined total of a set of numbers.

_______ **19.** An individual asks you open-ended questions about your spending habits and the stores you visit. Which type of research is this?

A. a questionnaire

B. an interview

C. a case study

D. participant observation

_______ **20.** Which of the following is necessary when determining a causal relationship between two variables?

A. The two variables must not be correlated.

B. All other possible factors must be ignored.

C. Empirical data must show one event caused another event.

D. Empirical data must be excluded from collection.

Chapter 2 Test, Form B *cont.*

networks

Sociological Research Methods

DIRECTIONS: Essay Answer each of the following questions.

21. Sociological research is designed to identify facts, verify evidence, and make theoretical assumptions about abstract variables. Why is it important to develop a research plan prior to testing theory?

"Sociologists respect the rights, dignity, and worth of all people. They strive to eliminate bias in their professional activities, and they do not tolerate any forms of discrimination based on age, gender; race, ethnicity; national origin; religion; sexual orientation; disability; health conditions; or marital, domestic, or parental status."

—*from* American Sociological Association's Code of Ethics

Credit: *American Sociological Association Code of Ethics*. Copyright © 1999 by The American Sociological Association. Reprinted by permission of the ASA.

22. Why are these statements of principle so important to sociologists? How can sociologists work to meet this standard?

NAME ________________________________ DATE ____________________ CLASS __________

Lesson Quiz 3-1

networks

Culture

DIRECTIONS: True/False In the blank, indicate whether the statement is true (T) or false (F).

_______ **1.** Because they are more intelligent, humans rely more on instincts than other animals.

_______ **2.** Cultural behavior must be learned.

_______ **3.** Animals are born with instincts.

_______ **4.** Individuals inherit specific personality traits and patterns of behavior.

_______ **5.** One criticism of sociobiology is that it can lead to claims that are racist.

DIRECTIONS: Multiple Choice Indicate the answer choice that best completes the statement or answers the question.

_______ **6.** How do sociobiologists view human behavior?

A. They differentiate human behavior from the behavior of animals.

B. They assume that behavior is biologically based and transmitted genetically.

C. They claim that human behavior is mostly shaped by environmental factors.

D. They argue that human behavior is based on observations of animal behavior.

_______ **7.** What are drives?

A. automatic reactions to physical stimuli

B. impulses to reduce discomfort

C. a form of human intelligence

D. learned behavior unique to humans

_______ **8.** How do sociologists view the role of culture in human behavior?

A. Culture guides the process of evolution.

B. Culture helps modify human instincts.

C. Culture helps direct the process of heredity.

D. Culture channels the expression of biological characteristics.

_______ **9.** How do sociologists define society?

A. people that share the same language

B. the combined genetic characteristics of a group of people

C. a territory inhabited by people with a common culture

D. the basis for human and nonhuman groups

_______ **10.** Which of the following is an element of culture?

A. instincts

B. values

C. reflexes

D. genetics

NAME ______________________________ DATE ________________ CLASS __________

Lesson Quiz 3-2

networks

Culture

DIRECTIONS: True/False In the blank, indicate whether the statement is true (T) or false (F).

________ **1.** The hypothesis of linguistic relativity states that the language we use influences our perception of the world.

________ **2.** The meaning of a symbol is based solely on its physical characteristics.

________ **3.** The vocabulary used by a society can reveal the level of sophistication of the society's culture.

________ **4.** People who begin to learn a new language often start to view the world differently.

________ **5.** A bell ringing at lunchtime is an example of a symbol.

DIRECTIONS: Multiple Choice Indicate the answer choice that best completes the statement or answers the question.

________ **6.** Which of the following is a symbol?

A. your school's mascot
B. drinking when thirsty
C. voting in a school election
D. being punished for skipping school

________ **7.** What is one way that language relates to culture?

A. Language hinders people from understanding their culture.
B. Language separates the culture of humans from that of animals.
C. Language enables culture to be transmitted from one generation to the next.
D. Language keeps each culture separate from all other cultures.

________ **8.** Which of the following best describes symbols?

A. the physical characteristics of something meaningful
B. things that stand for or represent something else
C. the sound you hear when words are spoken
D. only the spoken and written words of a language

________ **9.** Which of the following describes the hypothesis of linguistic relativity?

A. Language has no bearing on how we perceive the world.
B. Perception of reality remains the same despite language.
C. Our perception of reality depends largely on language.
D. All languages derive from our perception of reality.

________ **10.** What is one advantage of language for humans?

A. It helps humans develop drives and reflexes.
B. It frees humans from the limits of time and place.
C. It separates humans into distinct social groups.
D. It alters the genetic characteristics of humans.

Lesson Quiz 3-3

networks

Culture

DIRECTIONS: Matching Match each item with the correct statement below.

_____ **1.** norms that lack moral significance

_____ **2.** rules of behavior that bring punishment when they are violated

_____ **3.** sanctions that can be applied by most members of a group

_____ **4.** sanctions that are imposed by persons that are given special authority

_____ **5.** norms that have great moral significance and should be followed

A. formal sanctions

B. taboos

C. mores

D. folkways

E. informal sanctions

DIRECTIONS: Multiple Choice Indicate the answer choice that best completes the statement or answers the question.

_____ **6.** In the United States, most people believe that every child is entitled to an education. Which of the following is this belief an example of?

A. subculture
B. instinct
C. value
D. taboo

_____ **7.** Carlos's first-grade teacher is teaching him that he should speak in class only after raising his hand and being called on. What is this an example of?

A. norm
B. drive
C. taboo
D. subculture

_____ **8.** In the 1960s, African Americans boycotted some businesses that practiced segregation. Which of the following is this an example of?

A. a value
B. an informal sanction
C. a law
D. a formal sanction

_____ **9.** What is one value that has changed over time in the United States?

A. Openly expressed racism has increased.
B. The focus on earning a great deal of money has decreased.
C. There is a decline of openly expressed racism.
D. It is acceptable to base a promotion on favoritism, not competence.

_____ **10.** Which of the following is an example of a basic value or values in the United States?

A. segregation
B. unemployment
C. achievement and success
D. inherited rights and privileges

Lesson Quiz 3-4

Culture

DIRECTIONS: True/False In the blank, indicate whether the statement is true (T) or false (F).

________ **1.** In most societies, the real culture is identical to the ideal culture.

________ **2.** The importance that many people in the United States place on having nice cars is an example of a material aspect of culture.

________ **3.** Our ideal culture provides us with high standards of behavior.

________ **4.** Beliefs are always true.

________ **5.** The cultural meaning of physical objects is not determined by their physical characteristics.

DIRECTIONS: Multiple Choice Indicate the answer choice that best completes the statement or answers the question.

________ **6.** Which of the following is an example of a nonmaterial aspect of culture?

A. family relationships
B. houses
C. pizza parlors
D. computers

________ **7.** Assume that most members of a particular society believe everyone should have the same opportunities regardless of their race. In reality, however, many people discriminate against members of minority groups. Which of the following best describes this situation?

A. This society's formal sanctions are stronger than its informal sanctions.
B. This society believes that environment has a stronger influence than heredity.
C. The actual culture is different from the ideal culture.
D. These people are not ethnocentric.

________ **8.** Which of the following statements helps explain why beliefs are important?

A. People base their behavior on their beliefs.
B. Beliefs enable us to understand how the world works.
C. People use beliefs to know what is true.
D. Beliefs are an important part of material culture.

________ **9.** Which of the following is an example of how material culture can relate to nonmaterial culture?

A. buying the latest brand of sneakers to look cool
B. wearing a coat to keep warm in winter
C. getting a new computer because the old one no longer works
D. riding a bicycle to get to school in the morning

________ **10.** How does material culture differ from nonmaterial culture?

A. Only material culture gives meaning to physical objects.
B. Material culture consists of objects rather than beliefs and ideas.
C. Nonmaterial culture has no relationship with physical objects.
D. Material culture involves ideas, concepts and beliefs.

NAME _______________ DATE _______________ CLASS _______________

Lesson Quiz 3-5

networks

Culture

DIRECTIONS: Matching Match each item with the correct statement below.

_____ **1.** group that deliberately opposes the beliefs of the dominant culture

_____ **2.** a method of judging others by one's own cultural standards

_____ **3.** the borrowing of aspects of one culture by other cultures

_____ **4.** a group that is part of the dominant culture but differs from it in some ways

_____ **5.** groupings of people who share a social characteristic

A. social categories
B. counterculture
C. subculture
D. ethnocentrism
E. diffusion

DIRECTIONS: Multiple Choice Indicate the answer choice that best completes the statement or answers the question.

_____ **6.** What accounts for the presence of cultural universals?

A. rules of etiquette
B. biological differences
C. biological similarities
D. religious rituals

_____ **7.** In Sara's culture, women are expected to serve food to men. Then women eat their own meal after the men are finished eating. Which of the following is this an example of?

A. drive
B. cultural particular
C. violation of a norm
D. cultural universal

_____ **8.** Which of the following is an example of a cultural universal?

A. the existence of a family structure
B. lack of mourning rituals
C. tasks are not assigned but are left to decisions made by individuals
D. societal values are formed by individual choices

_____ **9.** Which of the following accounts for the global popularity of Hollywood movies?

A. invention
B. discovery
C. counterculture
D. diffusion

_____ **10.** How does a counterculture differ from a subculture?

A. A counterculture deliberately opposes the beliefs of the dominant culture.
B. A subculture has fewer group members than a counterculture.
C. Subcultures consciously reject the beliefs of the dominant culture.
D. Countercultures target subcultures for criticism.

NAME ______________________ DATE ______________ CLASS __________

Chapter 3 Test, Form A

networks

Culture

DIRECTIONS: Matching Match each statement or item with the correct item below.

_______ **1.** cultural universals

_______ **2.** Sapir-Whorf hypothesis

_______ **3.** mores

_______ **4.** instincts

_______ **5.** beliefs

_______ **6.** counterculture

_______ **7.** values

_______ **8.** taboo

_______ **9.** ideal culture

_______ **10.** drive

A. norms that have moral dimensions

B. cultural traits that exist in all cultures

C. a rule of behavior whose violation calls for punishment

D. genetically inherited patterns of behavior

E. linguistic relativity

F. an impulse to reduce discomfort

G. a subculture opposed to beliefs of the dominant culture

H. broad ideas about what is good

I. cultural guidelines that group members claim to accept

J. ideas about the nature of reality

DIRECTIONS: Multiple Choice Indicate the answer choice that best completes the statement or answers the question.

_______ **11.** Which of the following best describes how sociologists view human behavior?

A. It involves both genetic and environmental factors.

B. It is mainly the consequence of genetic factors.

C. It is inherited from one generation to the next.

D. It is shaped mostly by environmental factors.

_______ **12.** Shing-Ling had to show up in court and pay a fine because a police officer caught her speeding. This is an example of a(n)

A. formal sanction.

B. folkway.

C. informal sanction.

D. taboo.

_______ **13.** Which of the following is an example of a symbol?

A. the books you use to study

B. the time you spend studying

C. your school colors

D. your schedule of classes

_______ **14.** Which of the following is necessary to an understanding of sociobiology?

A. natural selection

B. language formation

C. environmental factors

D. cultural differences

_______ **15.** The global popularity of hamburgers, tacos, and pizza is an example of which of the following?

A. cultural particular

B. diffusion

C. counterculture

D. discovery

_______ **16.** Pulling away upon touching a hot stove is an example of which of the following?

A. cultural belief **C.** reflex

B. drive **D.** norm

_______ **17.** When members of a high school believe their school is better than the one across town and have a strong athletic rivalry with that school, they are exhibiting

A. an informal sanction.

B. a norm.

C. ethnocentrism.

D. the violation of a taboo.

_______ **18.** Which of the following is an example of a counterculture?

A. punk rockers

B. high school football team

C. church group

D. marching band

_______ **19.** Lisa cheats when playing checkers. As a result, her friends have stopped playing this game with her. Which of the following is this an example of?

A. taboo

B. formal sanction

C. informal sanction

D. law

_______ **20.** In the United States, it is common for guests at weddings to throw rice at the newly married couple as they leave the ceremony. What is this an example of?

A. mores **C.** drive

B. taboo **D.** folkway

Chapter 3 Test, Form A *cont.*

networks

Culture

DIRECTIONS: Essay Answer the following questions on a separate sheet of paper.

21. Discuss how language affects culture and how culture relates to the development of norms and values. Define the terms culture, norms, and values in your response.

22. Culture is an explanation of and guide for social behavior, including language, emotions, and thinking in a variety of different situations. Explain some possible positive results of a multicultural educational program where curriculum and instruction are designed based solely on cultural backgrounds.

"Adolescents' relationships with their parents also undergo a stressful period during early and middle adolescence. This stress is often focused on issues of control within the family, which are renegotiated during this developmental period. By necessity, children's relationships with their parents are asymmetrical in terms of power and authority; but as children mature, they need to take more and more authority for themselves until they eventually leave their natal home and take full responsibility for their own lives. In the optimal situation, parents will reinforce and stimulate this process of growing autonomy, self-determination, and independence. However, it is likely that the renegotiating process . . .will not be smooth."

—Jacquelynne S. Eccles, from *Development During Adolescence,* 1993

Credit: *Development During Adolescence* by Jacquelynne S. Eccles, et al. © 1993 by the American Psychological Association. Used by permission of the American Psychological Association.

23. Read this passage from the work of Jacquelynne Eccles. Why did she describe adolescence as a stressful period? What are some issues of control in families? In what ways can these issues help both parents and adolescents reach an understanding of each other's concerns? How can the resolution of the issues help a young person?

Chapter 3 Test, Form B

networks

Culture

DIRECTIONS: Matching Match each statement or item with the correct item below.

______ **1.** reflexes	**A.** a process of change over time
______ **2.** real culture	**B.** actual behavior of members of a group
______ **3.** evolution	**C.** rewards and punishments that are used to foster norms
______ **4.** social categories	**D.** a group that is part of, yet different from, the dominant culture
______ **5.** subculture	**E.** groups of people who share a social characteristic
______ **6.** symbols	**F.** norms that are enforced by designated officials
______ **7.** cultural particulars	**G.** how we relate to tangible objects
______ **8.** material culture	**H.** ways in which a culture expresses universal traits
______ **9.** sanctions	**I.** things that are used to represent something else
______ **10.** laws	**J.** automatic reactions to physical stimuli that are inherited

DIRECTIONS: Multiple Choice Indicate the answer choice that best completes the statement or answers the question.

______ **11.** Which of the following is a type of norm?

A. language
B. instinct
C. more
D. invention

______ **12.** Which of the following is a consequence of exposure to another language?

A. Our perception of reality changes.
B. We lose our own sense of culture.
C. We no longer rely so much on symbols.
D. Our perception of reality is confirmed.

______ **13.** Which of the following is an example of nonmaterial culture?

A. a house
B. a skateboard
C. honesty
D. a notebook

______ **14.** Which of the following describes a belief of many sociobiologists?

A. Our behavior is largely based on genetics.
B. Our behavior is largely based on our environment.
C. Our language determines the way in which we view the world.
D. There are no cultural universals.

_______ **15.** Which of the following is a cultural universal?

A. female-headed households

B. the lack of an army during peacetime

C. family structure

D. male-headed households

_______ **16.** Assume that Michael's teacher has a rule that if a student talks out-of-turn three times in one day, that student must stay in for recess for the rest of the week. Which of the following methods is the teacher using to control student behavior?

A. folkway
C. sociobiology

B. informal sanction
D. formal sanction

_______ **17.** Which of the following includes the idea that a person's perception of the world is influenced by the language she or he speaks?

A. cultural universal theory

B. culture/counterculture theory

C. Sapir-Whorf hypothesis

D. informal sanctions hypothesis

_______ **18.** Which of the following is an advantage of ethnocentrism?

A. the destabilization of certain parts of society

B. people in the majority are able to adopt the views of people in the minority

C. the likelihood that people will more likely uphold values

D. it can lead to divisions and discrimination immigrants

_______ **19.** Which of the following is a criticism of sociobiology?

A. It relies too heavily on environmental factors.

B. Sociobiology does not take evolution into account.

C. It could be used to label some races as superior to others.

D. Sociobiology fails to account for intelligence in animals.

_______ **20.** Which of the following are a basic value or values of the United States?

A. achievement and success

B. group superiority and a caste system

C. lack of democratic institution

D. forced religious belief

DIRECTIONS: Essay Answer the following questions on a separate sheet of paper.

21. Clarify how folkways, mores, and laws vary in importance within American society.

22. Some people feel that the American fast food industry is the best modern example of cultural diffusion. What other examples might be used to illustrate cultural diffusion?

Dos and Don'ts

Knowing the norms and customs of other nations may prevent embarrassing moments as you travel the world.

Country	Custom
Brazil	When accepting an invitation to a Brazilian home, arrive at least a half-hour late if you are coming to dinner and around an hour late if you are attending a party. Be sure to bring flowers as a hostess gift, but avoid purple flowers. They are used for funerals.
Bulgaria	Give only an odd number of gifts to a newborn baby. If dining in a Bulgarian home, take only a small portion of food for your first serving—guests show their appreciation for their host's hospitality by eating several servings. An empty glass will always be filled, so if you are done with your beverage, leave a mouthful of it in your glass.
Ghana	A Ghanaian handshake involves clasping right hands as in the United States, but then the people greeting each other twist their middle fingers and click them together. If you are not familiar with this greeting, it's best to stick to a traditional, straightforward handshake!
India	If your Indian hosts invite you to dinner, arrive on time. Etiquette demands that you remove your shoes before you enter the home. Do not accept items of food or a beverage the first time your host asks. Food and drink will be offered several times, and refusing the first time is simply good manners.
Japan	Remove your shoes when entering a Japanese home, and put on the slippers provided for guests. Make sure your shoes point away from the doorway through which you will enter. When using chopsticks, take care never to use them to point with. Do not rest the chopsticks on your plate, but lay them on the rest provided by your plate when you are not using them. Never, ever cross them!
New Zealand	The Maori—the indigenous peoples of New Zealand—have an elaborate protocol for greeting guests from outside their group. It is called a Powhiri, and it involves welcoming speechmaking that can last up to several hours. The Powhiri is followed by a meal. After the meal, it is considered good manners to thank those who have cooked and served the meal. This may result in a request to sing. Singing a song that represents your home country is a way to show gratitude and respect.
Norway	If you are bringing flowers as a hostess gift to a Norwegian home, have the flowers sent the morning of the meal so that they can be put on display before guests arrive. Always arrange for an odd number of flowers, and never send lilies, carnations, or any white flowers, as those are reserved for funerals.
Saudi Arabia	Saudis rarely entertain those from outside their culture in their homes unless they know them very well. As a visitor to a Saudi home, you should greet the older members of the host family first. Meals are often eaten with the fingers, but use only your right hand, as Saudis believe the left hand is unclean. Sample everything that is offered, but do not be surprised if the most valued food items—such as a sheep's head—are reserved just for you!

Source: Kwintessential, *Country Profiles: Global Guide to Culture, Customs and Etiquette*

23. The table shows the norms and customs of several different countries. Pick one country and describe how their norms and customs are identical to, or different from customs that are commonly observed in the United States. What do most of these norms and customs relate to? Why do you think the customs are different in different countries?

NAME ______________________________ DATE ______________ CLASS __________

Lesson Quiz 4-1

networks

Socialization

DIRECTIONS: True/False In the blank, indicate whether the statement is true (T) or false (F).

_______ **1.** Unlike other animals, humans are already socialized when they are born.

_______ **2.** The emotional needs of human infants are as important as their physical needs.

_______ **3.** With socialization, an individual is unable to learn beliefs and values.

_______ **4.** Even children who have experienced extreme isolation can learn some degree of socialization.

_______ **5.** The process of socialization requires prolonged social contact with others.

DIRECTIONS: Multiple Choice Indicate the answer choice that best completes the statement or answers the question.

_______ **6.** Socialization begins at birth and continues

A. until age 12.

B. until age 21.

C. until middle age.

D. throughout life.

_______ **7.** Which of the following is an emotional need of human infants?

A. food

B. control

C. affection

D. protection

_______ **8.** Which of the following best describes the results of Harry Harlow's research on rhesus monkeys?

A. The monkeys nearly always stayed with the wire mother because it was the one with the food.

B. The monkeys starved to death because they stayed with the terrycloth-covered mother and did not go to the wire mother that had food.

C. The monkeys primarily stayed with the terrycloth-covered mother, only going to the wire monkey for food.

D. The monkeys showed no preference for one mother over the other.

_______ **9.** The case histories of Anna, Isabelle, and Genie showed

A. how important socialization is to development.

B. the way that socialization may occur even in isolation.

C. the effects of prolonged and intensive human contact.

D. how development is independent of socialization.

_______ **10.** Socialization takes place through a process of cultural

A. isolation.

B. diffusion.

C. transmission.

D. development.

Lesson Quiz 4-2

networks

Socialization

DIRECTIONS: Matching Match each item with the correct statement below.

______ **1.** according to Mead, this is the part of the self that is spontaneous, unpredictable, and creative

______ **2.** the time around one-and-a-half years of age when a child starts mimicking the behavior of others

______ **3.** an image of yourself as having an identity unique from other people

______ **4.** according to Mead, the part of the self that is created through socialization

______ **5.** the time during which preschoolers begin to engage in sophisticated role taking

A. imitation stage

B. game stage

C. self concept

D. "I"

E. "me"

DIRECTIONS: Multiple Choice Indicate the answer choice that best completes the statement or answers the question.

______ **6.** ______________ holds that society exists because it is necessary to teach children to work together to create a stable society.

A. Functionalism
B. Conflict theory
C. Symbolic interactionism
D. Role-taking theory

______ **7.** Our self-concept

A. allows us to have an image of ourselves that is separate from those around us.
B. has little to do with how others see us.
C. stays the same throughout our lives.
D. is something we are born with and has nothing to do with the ways others interact with us.

______ **8.** Which of the following is a concept that is important in symbolic interactionism?

A. significant others
B. the importance of society norms
C. maintaining the status quo
D. the self-concept

______ **9.** Why is taking on a "role" important?

A. It allows us to determine who our important family members are.
B. It allows us to view ourselves through someone else's eyes.
C. It teaches us skills that protect us later in life.
D. It prevents us from considering the thoughts of others.

______ **10.** A child learns how to behave within her family by watching how her parents judge her behavior and then judging herself accordingly. Charles Horton Cooley called this process

A. desocialization.
B. resocialization.
C. the play stage.
D. the looking-glass self.

NAME ______________________ DATE ______________ CLASS __________

Lesson Quiz 4-3

networks

Socialization

DIRECTIONS: True/False In the blank, indicate whether the statement is true (T) or false (F).

_______ **1.** A 12-year-old's significant others include children who are in her peer group.

_______ **2.** Mass media plays a role in the socialization of children because it is constantly displaying role models that children may imitate.

_______ **3.** Children only belong to one peer group at a time.

_______ **4.** The primary agent of socialization in the United States is the family.

_______ **5.** Religion has little influence on how children are socialized to learn aspects of group life, such as work and proper gender roles.

DIRECTIONS: Multiple Choice Indicate the answer choice that best completes the statement or answers the question.

_______ **6.** Which of the following is an example of a hidden curriculum at most schools?

A. acting a role in a play

B. reading a poem

C. learning the rules of a game

D. learning to behave

_______ **7.** _______________ is the only agency of socialization that is not controlled primarily by adults.

A. A peer group

B. Mass media

C. Family

D. School

_______ **8.** Which of the following is one way that religion serves as an agent for socialization?

A. It shows students how to learn more effectively.

B. It evaluates children on the basis of objective standards.

C. It teaches children morals and beliefs.

D. It prevents children from being isolated.

_______ **9.** Mass media plays a role in socialization by

A. providing entertainment to keep children busy.

B. offering a substitute for human contact.

C. displaying role models for children to imitate.

D. providing an alternative to formal education.

_______ **10.** Which of the following most influences the role of the family in socialization?

A. use of transportation

B. age of parents

C. number of children

D. social class

NAME ______________________________ DATE ______________ CLASS __________

Lesson Quiz 4-4

networks

Socialization

DIRECTIONS: Matching Match each item with the correct statement below.

_______ **1.** the period that occurs after high school, but before adulthood

_______ **2.** a change in one's attitudes or beliefs

_______ **3.** rituals that mark the shift from one status to another

_______ **4.** the stage between childhood and adulthood

_______ **5.** the stages of development from birth to death

A. life cycle

B. adolescence

C. transitional adulthood

D. rites of passage

E. reorientation

DIRECTIONS: Multiple Choice Indicate the answer choice that best completes the statement or answers the question.

_______ **6.** Which of the following is a challenge usually associated with adolescence?

A. decreased decision making opportunities

B. a firm grasp of one's status

C. a lowering of feelings of pressure

D. pressure from a peer group

_______ **7.** Which of the following helps explain the development of adolescence as a stage in the life cycle?

A. a universal education system

B. the eradication of social class

C. the shift from industry to technology

D. the gradual exclusion of children from the workforce

_______ **8.** During the middle years a person's emphasis often shifts from

A. a focus on the present to memories of the past.

B. how far he or she has come to how much time may be left.

C. family to professional concerns.

D. adult to adolescent concerns.

_______ **9.** Why are the early middle years often particularly stressful for women?

A. They have to balance the need for income with retirement.

B. They pursue the role of student and employee.

C. They face the demands of dating and school.

D. They often juggle the roles of parent and employee.

_______ **10.** How has the perception of old age changed?

A. Life expectancy has remained the same over the past 50 years.

B. Old age occurs later in life.

C. Elderly people now have rights.

D. Old age means that people leave the work force earlier.

NAME ______________________ DATE ______________ CLASS ____________

Lesson Quiz 4-5

networks

Socialization

DIRECTIONS: Modified True/False In the blank, indicate whether the statement is true (T) or false (F). If false, edit the statement to make it a true statement.

_______ **1.** A public university is one example of a total institution.

____

_______ **2.** Total institutions use desocialization to destroy old self-concepts of identity.

____

_______ **3.** A system of rewards and punishments is one way a total institution resocializes people.

____

_______ **4.** People rarely use peer groups as a tool for anticipatory socialization.

____

_______ **5.** Anticipatory socialization often occurs in prisons and other total institutions.

____

DIRECTIONS: Multiple Choice Indicate the answer choice that best completes the statement or answers the question.

_______ **6.** Which of the following is a way that a total institution typically desocializes members of a group?

A. by letting them spend a great deal of unsupervised time with peer groups
B. by allowing them to have visitors whenever they want
C. by requiring that they all dress alike
D. by giving them a great deal of privacy

_______ **7.** When pre-teens look to adolescents as a model of values and behavior, they are using

A. resocialization.
B. anticipatory socialization
C. a reference group.
D. a total institution.

_______ **8.** Paul has just gotten married and is looking forward to his new life as a husband. This is an example of

A. the looking-glass self.
B. the imagination stage.
C. the game stage.
D. anticipatory socialization.

_______ **9.** When a person is a resident of a total institution, the first step in attempting to change the person is

A. desocialization.
B. resocialization.
C. role-taking.
D. anticipatory socialization.

_______ **10.** Which of the following is an example of a total institution?

A. summer camp for teenagers
B. restaurant
C. military boot camp
D. scout troop

Chapter 4 Test, Form A

networks

Socialization

DIRECTIONS: Matching Match each item with the correct statement below.

_______ **1.** children begin to copy behavior without knowing why

_______ **2.** the part of the self that is spontaneous and creative

_______ **3.** stages of development between birth and death

_______ **4.** the part of the self that is created through socialization

_______ **5.** the process of learning to participate in group life

_______ **6.** group you use to evaluate yourself

_______ **7.** integrated conception of the norms, values, and beliefs of one's community

_______ **8.** stage of development between childhood and adulthood

_______ **9.** the condition of being set apart from others

_______ **10.** set of individuals of about the same age and having similar interests

A. "I"

B. life cycle

C. peer group

D. socialization

E. "me"

F. reference group

G. adolescence

H. imitation stage

I. generalized other

J. isolation

DIRECTIONS: Multiple Choice Indicate the answer choice that best completes the statement or answers the question.

_______ **11.** Which of the following is generally the first agent of socialization for most people?

A. family
B. mass media
C. religion
D. medicine

_______ **12.** Which of the following is one of the stages of grieving?

A. sorrow
B. crying
C. fear
D. depression

_______ **13.** Which of the following is an example of a peer group?

A. students and teachers
B. children and parents
C. classmates and friends
D. players and coaches

______ **14.** __________ views socialization as a way of teaching the child his or her social class and therefore maintaining the status quo.

A. Functionalism

B. Conflict theory

C. Symbolic interactionism

D. Role-taking theory

______ **15.** Aman is graduating from college and looking forward to his new role in his job as a computer scientist for a large firm. This is an example of

A. resocialization.

B. anticipatory socialization.

C. the imagination stage.

D. the game stage.

______ **16.** Which of the following is an example of a total institution?

A. a day camp

B. a prison

C. a public university

D. a hospital emergency room

______ **17.** You want to do research on the effects of human interaction on a group of kittens. You divide the group in half; one half is played with for an hour, twice a day. The other group has no human interaction. Both groups of kittens can play among themselves as much as they wish. The group that is played with by humans is the __________ group.

A. control

B. experimental

C. functional

D. socialized

______ **18.** What did Mead call the part of the self that is created during socialization?

A. role-taking self

B. the "me"

C. the "I"

D. the generalized self

______ **19.** Which of the following is important to develop during adolescence?

A. large motor skills

B. parenting skills

C. courtship skills

D. critical thinking skills

_______ **20.** You want to do research on the effects of a weight-lifting program on a group of high school students. You divide the group in half; one half performs the program three times a week, the second group continues on with their normal routine. The group that continues on with its normal routine is the ____________ group.

A. socialized

B. control

C. experimental

D. functional

DIRECTIONS: Essays Answer the following questions on a separate sheet of paper.

21. Define socialization. Include and discuss examples of its significance and importance to American culture.

22. Using the concept of hidden curriculum, describe the socialization process of American students in public and/or private schools.

"From her father's perspective, the mere fact of having boyfriends is rebellious, but Charisse still manages to have a very full social life when it comes to boys. Many of Charisse's male interests are older than she, and irregularly employed—although some are in and out of school. She meets many of them hanging out at the mall."

—from Mary Pattillo-McCoy, *Black Picket Fences: Privilege and Peril Among the Black Middle Class,* 1999

23. The paragraph above outlines some of the reasons conflicts arise between teenagers and their parents. What behaviors are shown by Charisse and her father that might be characterized as "typical" during a child's adolescence? Explain.

NAME ______________________________ DATE ______________ CLASS __________

Chapter 4 Test, Form B

networks

Socialization

DIRECTIONS: Matching Match each item with the correct statement below.

______ **1.** learning to participate in group life	**A.** role taking
______ **2.** places where people are separated from the rest of society	**B.** socialization
______ **3.** assuming the viewpoint of another person to shape the self-concept	**C.** rites of passage
	D. play stage
______ **4.** rituals that mark the shift from one stage of development to another	**E.** desocialization
______ **5.** process of giving up old values, beliefs, and behaviors	**F.** self-concept
______ **6.** means of communication designed to reach the general population	**G.** hidden curriculum
	H. mass media
______ **7.** an image of yourself as having an identity different from others	**I.** peer group
______ **8.** unofficial aspects of culture that children are taught in school	**J.** total institutions
______ **9.** children acting in ways they imagine other people would act	
______ **10.** individuals of roughly the same age and with similar interests	

DIRECTIONS: Multiple Choice Indicate the answer choice that best completes the statement or answers the question.

______ **11.** Which of the following is typically the longest stage in a human life cycle?

A. adolescence

B. childhood

C. old age

D. adulthood

______ **12.** Many experts on human development believe

A. that humans develop normally with little contact with other humans.

B. human babies without close human contact have difficulty forming emotional ties with other people.

C. that it is easy to draw conclusions about human behavior from observing the behavior of other animals

D. unlike other animals, human do not have emotional needs, only physiological needs.

______ **13.** Functionalism states that network television is a force for social stability because

A. it functions as a looking-glass self.

B. everyone is exposed to the same shared beliefs and values.

C. the people who express opinions on television exert power over the community, helping to institute change.

D. it encourages the sharing of various social and political views.

Chapter 4 Test, Form B *cont.*

Socialization

_______ **14.** In school, rewards and punishments are typically based on

A. performance.

B. affection.

C. blood relationships.

D. desocialization.

_______ **15.** Which of the following probably would be a significant other in the life of a four-year-old girl living in a two-parent home?

A. her friend's mother

B. her father

C. her mother's boss

D. a policewoman

_______ **16.** Role taking allows people to

A. practice for our role in life.

B. imagine that they act alone without the input of other people.

C. see themselves as other people see them.

D. skip the imitation stage of socialization.

_______ **17.** What did Mead call the part of the self that is creative, unpredictable, and spontaneous?

A. the role-taking self

B. the "me"

C. the "I"

D. the generalized self

_______ **18.** A _______ is made up of those people to whom we look to establish values and attitudes and whom we use to elevate ourselves.

A. play group

B. reference group

C. total institution

D. generalized group

_______ **19.** What is one thing that the hidden curriculum of schools teaches children?

A. conformity

B. art

C. science

D. history

_______ **20.** Which of the following best explains the difference between the game stage and the play stage?

A. The game stage is more sophisticated, with several participants being involved, each with a distinct role.

B. The play stage is more sophisticated because the child's values, beliefs, and attitudes start to depend on general concepts.

C. The play stage is less sophisticated because during this time all the child does is mimic the behavior of others without taking on any roles.

D. The game stage is less sophisticated because the child is not yet able to understand the concept of role taking.

Socialization

DIRECTIONS: Essay Answer the following questions on a separate sheet of paper.

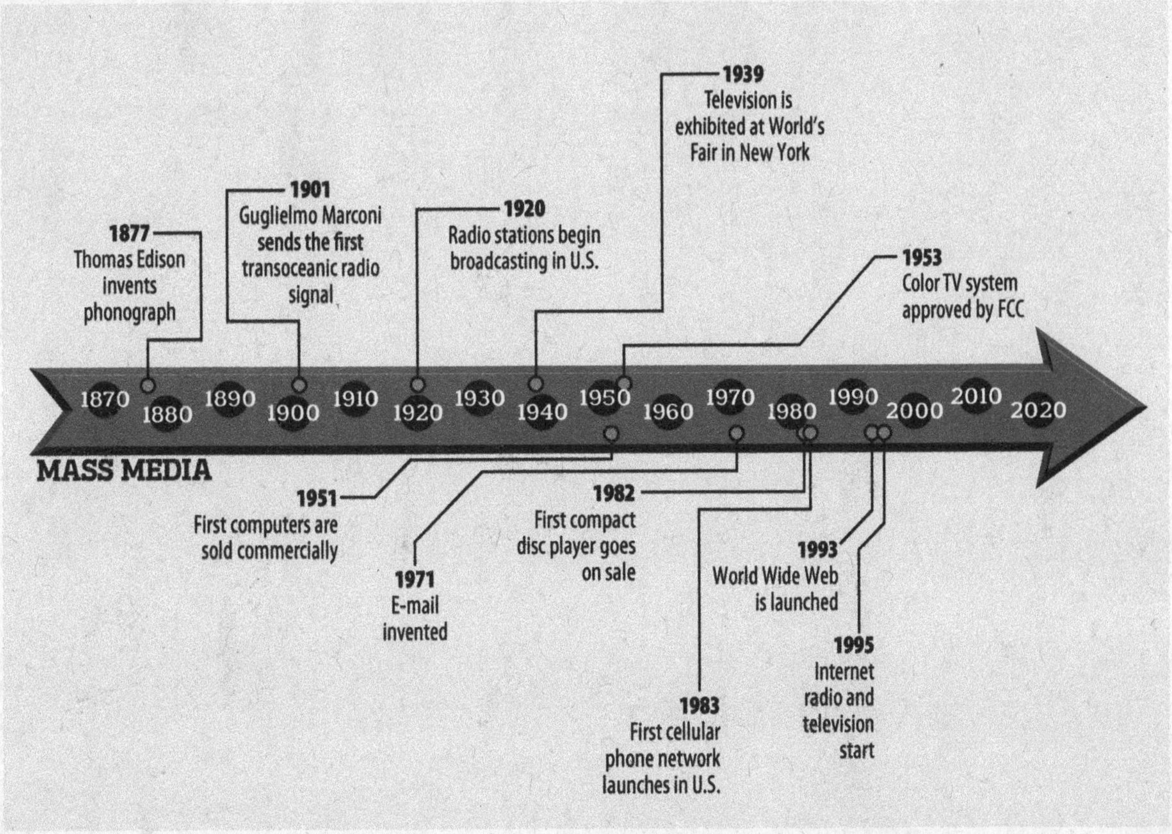
1877 Thomas Edison invents phonograph
1901 Guglielmo Marconi sends the first transoceanic radio signal
1920 Radio stations begin broadcasting in U.S.
1939 Television is exhibited at World's Fair in New York
1953 Color TV system approved by FCC
1870
1880
1890
1900
1910
1920
1930
1940
1950
1960
1970
1980
1990
2000
2010
2020
MASS MEDIA
1951 First computers are sold commercially
1971 E-mail invented
1982 First compact disc player goes on sale
1993 World Wide Web is launched
1995 Internet radio and television start
1983 First cellular phone network launches in U.S.

21. Look at the diagram above. Notice that print media—books, magazines, and newspapers—are not included in this time line. Why do you think they were omitted? Are they still relevant today?

22. In developing the symbolic interactionist perspective, George Herbert Mead pointed out that some people are more important to the development of our concept of self than others. He called these people significant others. What are some significant others in the lives of most people? Do they change during a person's life? How do they affect a person's development?

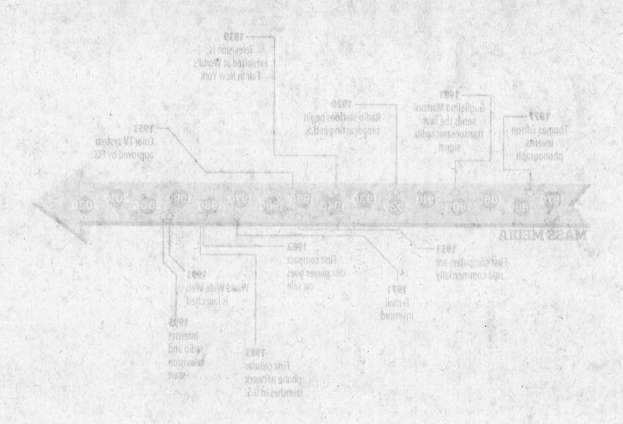

NAME ______________________ DATE ______________________ CLASS ______________

Lesson Quiz 5-1

networks

Social Structure and Society

DIRECTIONS: Modified True/False In the blank, indicate whether the statement is true (T) or false (F). If false, edit the statement to make it a true statement.

_______ **1.** The role of social structure is to help us see how we fit into a group.

____

_______ **2.** Deciding to get married is an example of an ascribed status.

____

_______ **3.** A status set might include being a college graduate, but would not include being an American citizen.

____

_______ **4.** Master statuses may be achieved or ascribed.

____

_______ **5.** An example of an achieved status is the decision to join the soccer team.

____

DIRECTIONS: Multiple Choice Indicate the answer choice that best completes the statement or answers the question.

_______ **6.** What is a term used to describe the status of a young child?

A. role
B. achieved
C. performance
D. ascribed

_______ **7.** When you join a sports team and are trying to determine the patterns of relationships among the members, you are determining the group's

A. master status.
B. social structure.
C. ascribed status.
D. role conflict.

_______ **8.** Which of the following is an example of an ascribed social status?

A. becoming a mother
B. being a member of a club
C. reaching the age to vote in a national election
D. striking up a friendship with a classmate

_______ **9.** A status set includes

A. all of the statuses a person occupies at any particular time.
B. only statuses that have been achieved.
C. some ascribed and achieved statuses.
D. mostly ascribed statuses.

_______ **10.** What is the difference between a master status and a status set?

A. Status sets can change while a master status remains the same.
B. A master status includes all of the other statuses a person occupies.
C. A master status is one important status within a status set.
D. A master status is a network of linked statuses.

Lesson Quiz 5-2

networks

Social Structure and Society

DIRECTIONS: Modified True/False In the blank, indicate whether the statement is true (T) or false (F). If false, edit the statement to make it a true statement.

_______ **1.** Role conflict can be reduced when we try to take a positive attitude when examining our situation.

____

_______ **2.** Because young people occupy no status positions in society, only adults can experience role strain.

____

_______ **3.** Rights are behaviors that people expect from others, while obligations are behaviors individuals perform toward others.

____

_______ **4.** Social interaction only involves important moments of interaction among people.

____

_______ **5.** Role performance can occur even when people are alone.

____

DIRECTIONS: Multiple Choice Indicate the answer choice that best completes the statement or answers the question.

_______ **6.** What term characterizes the phrase "A teacher has to be respected by her students."

A. right
B. conflict
C. obligation
D. status

_______ **7.** When the time you spend working at a fast-food restaurant causes you to do poorly on an American history test, you are experiencing

A. organic solidarity.
B. nomadism.
C. role strain.
D. role conflict.

_______ **8.** A student has to study the material presented by the teacher. What term characterizes this phrase?

A. an obligation
B. a conflict
C. a right
D. a status

_______ **9.** When you are discussing with your friend what to do on Friday night, you are engaging in

A. role conflict.
B. role strain.
C. social interaction.
D. mechanical solidarity.

_______ **10.** What term would best describe what occurs when a student presents a paper in class?

A. ascribed status
B. role conflict
C. role performance
D. role strain

NAME ________________________________ DATE ________________ CLASS ____________

Lesson Quiz 5-3

networks

Social Structure and Society

DIRECTIONS: Matching Match each item with the correct statement below.

________ **1.** subsists primarily by growing food with the help of plows and animals

________ **2.** a group of people living within defined borders that share a common culture

________ **3.** subsists primarily by raising animals

________ **4.** subsists by manual farming, without the aid of equipment or animals

________ **5.** survives by hunting animals and gathering naturally growing fruits and vegetables

A. pastoral society

B. agricultural society

C. horticultural society

D. hunting and gathering society

E. society

DIRECTIONS: Multiple Choice Indicate the answer choice that best completes the statement or answers the question.

________ **6.** The earliest type of society was a(n)

A. pastoral society.

B. hunting and gathering society.

C. agricultural society

D. industrial society.

________ **7.** Which of the following is the primary reason that people living in hunting and gathering societies were nomads?

A. They overused their fields so that the fields were no longer fertile, and they had to find new ones.

B. They had to move depending on the seasons and where food was located.

C. They were always at war with other groups and moved to avoid conflict.

D. They needed to be closer to urban areas.

________ **8.** A group of people who live in the mountains and whose primary work is herding sheep is an example of a(n)

A. pastoral society.

B. organic society.

C. horticultural society.

D. agricultural society.

________ **9.** Which of the following societies subsists by using plows to grow food and by domesticating animals?

A. pastoral society

B. agricultural society

C. hunting and gathering society

D. horticultural society

________ **10.** The smaller structures of a preindustrial society enable it to

A. rapidly adapt to changing conditions.

B. subsist using agriculture.

C. meet all the needs of its members.

D. evolve into a postindustrial society.

NAME ______________________ DATE ______________ CLASS __________

Lesson Quiz 5-4

networks

Social Structure and Society

DIRECTIONS: True/False In the blank, indicate whether the statement is true (T) or false (F).

______ **1.** Americans live in a postindustrial society.

______ **2.** In industrial societies, machines have replaced the power previously supplied by people and animals.

______ **3.** Organic solidarity is a type of social unity based on people doing the same type of work.

______ **4.** Ferdinand Tönnies used the term gemeinschaft to refer to industrial societies.

______ **5.** One reason that postindustrial societies may experience instability is the decline of traditional family structures.

DIRECTIONS: Multiple Choice Indicate the answer choice that best completes the statement or answers the question.

______ **6.** Which of the following is true of postindustrial societies?

A. More people work in white-collar jobs than in blue-collar jobs.
B. More people work in blue-collar jobs than in white-collar jobs.
C. People assess technological change primarily after introducing it.
D. Technical knowledge is less important in the workplace.

______ **7.** Which of the following is a characteristic of organic solidarity?

A. Social unity is achieved through a consensus of beliefs and values.
B. People have complex specialized statuses that make them interdependent.
C. There are stronger pressures to conform than in other societies.
D. There is little competition.

______ **8.** According to Ferdinand Tönnies, industrial societies are characterized by

A. a strong feeling of interconnectedness among people.
B. weak family ties.
C. very little competition.
D. more personal social relationships than in preindustrial societies.

______ **9.** Which of the following is true concerning American society?

A. We are living in a preindustrial society.
B. Because our roles are highly specialized, very few people experience role strain.
C. The pressure to conform to society's norms is higher than at earlier times in history.
D. In recent years, we have seen an increase in social stability.

______ **10.** Which of the following describes an industrial society?

A. mechanical solidarity
B. gesellschaft
C. organic solidarity
D. gemeinschaft

NAME ______________________ DATE ______________ CLASS __________

Chapter 5 Test, Form A

networks

Social Structure and Society

DIRECTIONS: Matching Match each item with the correct statement below.

_______ **1.** a behavior individuals are expected to perform toward others	**A.** pastoral society
_______ **2.** social unity based on people doing the same type of work	**B.** right
_______ **3.** a behavior that people expect from others	**C.** social structure
_______ **4.** a position that strongly influences aspects of a person's life	**D.** horticultural society
_______ **5.** the pattern of social relationships in a group	**E.** master status
_______ **6.** expected behavior that is associated with a particular status	**F.** organic solidarity
_______ **7.** a position in a social structure that is assigned	**G.** mechanical solidarity
_______ **8.** social unity based on specialized functions and statuses	**H.** role
_______ **9.** a social group that obtains food by using tools to grow plants	**I.** ascribed status
_______ **10.** a social group that raises animals as a primary means of obtaining food	**J.** obligation

DIRECTIONS: Multiple Choice Indicate the answer choice that best completes the statement or answers the question.

_______ **11.** When you discuss Sunday afternoon's football game with your brother, you are engaging in

A. role conflict.
B. role strain.
C. social interaction.
D. mechanical solidarity.

_______ **12.** Which of the following is included in a status set?

A. some achieved and some ascribed statuses
B. mostly ascribed statuses
C. all of the statuses a person occupies
D. only achieved statuses

_______ **13.** Which of the following is a consequence of the shift from a hunting and gathering society to a horticulture society?

A. an increase in migration
B. the creation of more permanent settlements
C. improved technology
D. movement from cities to rural areas

Chapter 5 Test, Form A *cont.*

Social Structure and Society

_______ **14.** When a new student tries to determine the patterns of relationships among her classmates, she is learning about the group's

A. master status.
B. social structure.
C. role performance.
D. status set.

_______ **15.** Which of the following is a characteristic of a postindustrial society?

A. White-collar work replaces blue-collar work.
B. The majority of the labor force is represented by a union.
C. Mechanical knowledge is the key-organizing feature.
D. Industrial processes create specialized work.

_______ **16.** Teenagers who have jobs that prevent them from studying are experiencing

A. social interaction.
B. role performance.
C. role strain.
D. role conflict.

_______ **17.** Deciding to join the chess club is an example of a(n)

A. master status.
B. status set.
C. ascribed status.
D. achieved status.

_______ **18.** Which of the following is an example of how industrialization changed family functions?

A. Economic activities move from factories to the home.
B. Women became more subordinate to men.
C. Education moves from the home to schools.
D. Mass-produced items replace processed goods.

_______ **19.** How do agricultural and horticultural societies differ?

A. Agricultural societies use animals and plows.
B. Only horticultural societies grow plants.
C. Horticultural societies create permanent settlements.
D. Most agricultural societies are nomadic.

_______ **20.** What term describes a problem parents have when they have to work and also take care of their children's basic needs?

A. role conflict
B. obligation
C. right
D. role strain

Chapter 5 Test, Form A *cont.*

Social Structure and Society

DIRECTIONS: Essay Answer the following questions on a separate sheet of paper.

21. Compare and contrast several predominant features of industrial and postindustrial societies.

22. Explain, using examples, the difference between rights and obligations that are attached to a status.

> "In an attempt to understand just what it means psychologically to be a prisoner or a prison guard, Craig Haney, Curt Banks, Dave Jaffe, and I created our own prison. We carefully screened over 70 volunteers who answered an ad in a Palo Alto city newspaper and ended up with about two dozen young men who were selected to be part of this study....
>
> Half were arbitrarily designated as prisoners by a flip of a coin, the others as guards....
>
> We had to release three prisoners in the first four days because they had such acute situational traumatic reactions such as hysterical crying, confusion in thinking, and severe depression....
>
> About a third of the guards become tyrannical in their arbitrary use of power, in enjoying their control over other people....
>
> By the end of the week the experiment had become a reality."
>
> —Phillip G. Zimbardo, "Pathology of Imprisonment," *Society*, April 1972
>
> *Pathology of Imprisonment* by Philip G. Zimbardo. Published by Society, April 1972. Used with permission.

23. This experiment showed how status is adopted in a controlled situation. What was the time frame involved in this experiment? Did the people "assume" their assigned roles quickly? In any society, there are people who might be described as timid or meek, and others who would be identified as aggressive. How did the investigators insure that people did not gravitate to specific "roles" in this experiment based on their normal personality traits? Why do you think this experiment was ended by the investigators?

Chapter 5 Test, Form B

networks

Social Structure and Society

DIRECTIONS: Matching Match each item with the correct statement below.

_______ **1.** a preindustrial society based on kinship and tradition

_______ **2.** an industrial society characterized by weak family ties and competition

_______ **3.** uses animals and plows to grow food

_______ **4.** survives by hunting animals and gathering fruits and vegetables

_______ **5.** behavior exhibited by people as they carry out a role

_______ **6.** all of the statuses a person occupies at a given time

_______ **7.** when a person has trouble meeting the many roles in a single status

_______ **8.** any of the processes by which people influence one another

_______ **9.** a position in a social structure that is earned or chosen

_______ **10.** expectations for performance of a role when one status clashes with another

A. role performance

B. agricultural society

C. hunting and gathering society

D. achieved status

E. role conflict

F. gemeinschaft

G. social interaction

H. status set

I. role strain

J. gesellschaft

DIRECTIONS: Multiple Choice Indicate the answer choice that best completes the statement or answers the question.

_______ **11.** Which of the following is an example of an ascribed status?

A. female

B. employee

C. friend

D. teammate

_______ **12.** A student who struggles to keep her grades up while also playing a sport and participating in other activities is experiencing

A. social interaction.

B. role conflict.

C. role strain.

D. role performance.

_______ **13.** Why do pastoral societies tend to be male dominated?

A. Pastoral societies tend to have larger populations of men.

B. Women remain at home while men herd the animals to new pastures.

C. Men hunt for meat while women gather fruits and vegetables.

D. Women farm while men herd cattle.

_______ **14.** In which of the following is urbanization most common?

A. pastoral society
B. horticultural society
C. agricultural society
D. industrial society

_______ **15.** Which of the following is an example of a right?

A. teachers expect students to listen in class
B. students do their assignments
C. parents feed their children
D. governments provide basic education

_______ **16.** Which of the following best describes how roles relate to statuses?

A. Status is the total set of roles a person has.
B. Roles are statuses in action.
C. Statuses describe behaviors.
D. Roles are positions that status sets in motion.

_______ **17.** In which society did increased productivity give rise to new political and social institutions?

A. pastoral
B. horticultural
C. hunting and gathering
D. agricultural

_______ **18.** The underlying pattern of social relationships within a group constitutes that group's social

A. status.
B. role.
C. interaction.
D. structure.

_______ **19.** What kind of society makes heavy use of mechanization?

A. horticultural
B. pastoral
C. industrial
D. hunting and gathering

_______ **20.** Being born female or male is an example of which type of status?

A. ascribed
B. achieved
C. master status
D. status set

DIRECTIONS: Essay Answer the following questions.

21. Identify and discuss the major elements of social structure.

____

____

____

____

____

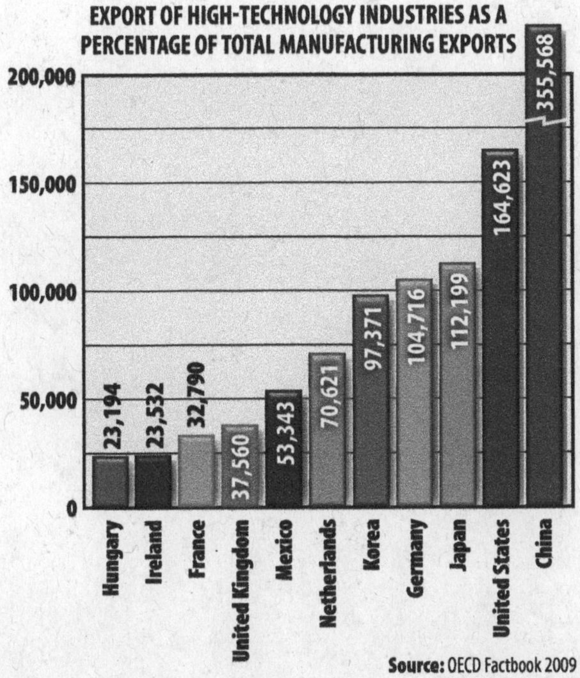

Source: OECD Factbook 2009

22. Look at the data in the chart. Which three countries appear to be the leaders in high-technology exports? What are some possible explanations for the leadership of these countries?

____

____

____

____

____

networks Chapter 5 Test, Form B cont.

Social Structure and Society

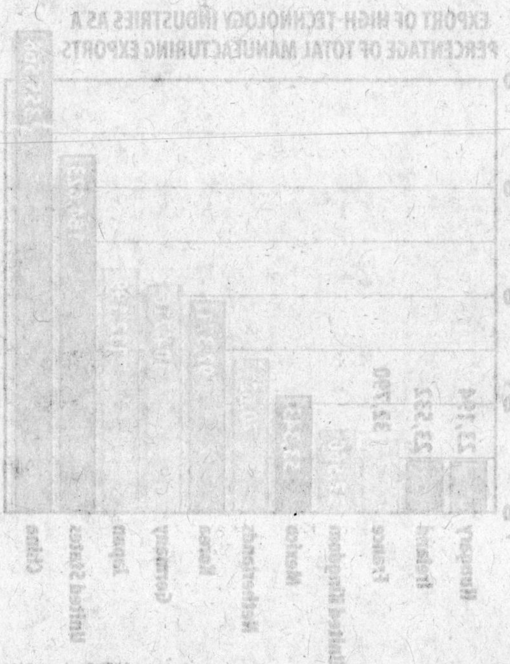

NAME ______________________________ DATE ______________ CLASS ________

Lesson Quiz 6-1

networks

Groups and Formal Organizations

DIRECTIONS: Modified True/False In the blank, indicate whether the statement is true (T) or false (F). If false, edit the statement to make it a true statement.

_______ **1.** One difference between a group and a social category is that the members of a group must interact with one another while those in a social category need not.

____

_______ **2.** The members of a social aggregate must all have similar social statuses.

____

_______ **3.** Family and childhood playgroups are the first primary groups.

____

_______ **4.** One reason secondary groups form is because members want to accomplish a specific task.

____

_______ **5.** Primary relationships develop more easily in large groups.

____

DIRECTIONS: Multiple Choice Indicate the answer choice that best completes the statement or answers the question.

_______ **6.** Those people present at a grocery store when a fire starts are an example of a

A. secondary group.
B. primary group.
C. social aggregate.
D. social category.

_______ **7.** Retired people are an example of a

A. secondary group.
B. primary group.
C. social aggregate.
D. social category.

_______ **8.** Which of the following is an integral part of the development of a secondary group?

A. face-to-face contact
B. continuous contact
C. a shared goal
D. a proper social environment

_______ **9.** Which of the following helps explain the difference between groups and social categories?

A. Groups are people with a shared social characteristic.
B. Members of social categories require close contact.
C. Members of a social category may never meet or interact.
D. Social categories can be informal or formal.

_______ **10.** You are buying a house and have several appointments with your lawyer to complete the necessary paperwork. This is an example of a

A. secondary relationship.
B. primary relationship.
C. social aggregate.
D. social category.

NAME ______________________ DATE ______________ CLASS __________

Lesson Quiz 6-2

networks

Groups and Formal Organizations

DIRECTIONS: Modified True/False In the blank, indicate whether the statement is true (T) or false (F). If false, edit the statement to make it a true statement.

_______ **1.** One membership role of in-group members is to feel opposition toward the out-group.

____

_______ **2.** In order to use a reference group to evaluate yourself, you need to be a member of that group.

____

_______ **3.** Social networks include all of the primary and secondary groups a person belongs to.

____

_______ **4.** One characteristic of a social network is that it forms clear group boundaries.

____

_______ **5.** Technology such as cell phones and computers help connect people to social networks.

____

DIRECTIONS: Multiple Choice Indicate the answer choice that best completes the statement or answers the question.

_______ **6.** Which of the following is a characteristic of a social network?

A. A social network includes only primary groups.
B. A social network dilutes relationships by bringing in many members.
C. A social network can provide a sense of belonging and purpose.
D. A social network involves close and continuous contact among members.

_______ **7.** Which of the following best describes the relationship between in-groups and out-groups?

A. You can't have one without the other.
B. One has nothing to do with the other.
C. Both groups form a harmonious unit.
D. The two groups lack a clear boundary.

_______ **8.** How might in-group members identify one another?

A. by clapping
B. by using a special handshake
C. by using first names only
D. by waving hello

_______ **9.** Why do people use reference groups?

A. People use them to evaluate themselves and acquire values.
B. Reference groups give people something to join.
C. They provide models of positive behavior.
D. People use reference groups to exclude others.

_______ **10.** What is one way a social network differs from a group?

A. A group is made up of social networks.
B. A social network is made up of groups.
C. A group lacks clear boundaries.
D. A social network relies on intimate relationships.

Lesson Quiz 6-3

networks

Groups and Formal Organizations

DIRECTIONS: Matching Match each item with the correct statement below.

A. conformity
B. conflict
C. social exchange
D. coercion
E. cooperation

_______ **1.** cutting your hair short because that's how your friends wear their hair

_______ **2.** helping a classmate study for an algebra test in return for his or her loan of a car for Saturday night

_______ **3.** club members having a car wash to raise money for cancer research

_______ **4.** fighting with your brother over how you should split the money both of you earned raking leaves

_______ **5.** Pat's parents telling her she can keep her job only if she raises her grade point average to 3.0

DIRECTIONS: Multiple Choice Indicate the answer choice that best completes the statement or answers the question.

_______ **6.** Workers at an insurance company are expected to work five hours of overtime a week without extra pay. If they do not, the boss has implied they will probably never receive a promotion. Which of the following describes this situation?

A. cooperation
B. coercion
C. conflict
D. conformity

_______ **7.** According to conflict theory, which of the following is the main method of controlling conflict in prisons?

A. the superior power of the guards
B. the desire on the part of the inmates to get along with one another
C. cable television
D. training programs offered to inmates to further their education

_______ **8.** When one of the maids on a motel's staff is not feeling well, it is understood that the other maids will help her out by doing part of her work. This is an example of

A. social exchange.
B. conflict.
C. conformity.
D. coercion.

_______ **9.** How does coercion differ from social exchange?

A. In coercion one party is clearly dominant.
B. Actions are voluntary in coercion.
C. People engage in coercion for mutual benefit.
D. Coercion involves parties who are equal.

_______ **10.** Which of the following best expresses conformity?

A. What do you think?
B. That's a bad idea.
C. Let's talk this over.
D. All my friends say I should!

NAME ______________________ DATE ______________ CLASS __________

Lesson Quiz 6-4

networks

Groups and Formal Organizations

DIRECTIONS: True/False In the blank, indicate whether the statement is true (T) or false (F).

________ **1.** Informal groups are created because people's needs are not being met by any formal group.

________ **2.** Bureaucracies are rarely seen in postindustrial societies because computers have made them obsolete.

________ **3.** According to the Iron Law of Oligarchy, power tends to concentrate in the hands of fewer and fewer people.

________ **4.** In a bureaucracy, people are encouraged to avoid specialization.

________ **5.** One advantage of a bureaucracy is that it protects people from arbitrary decisions.

DIRECTIONS: Multiple Choice Indicate the answer choice that best completes the statement or answers the question.

________ **6.** What did Max Weber say was an advantage of bureaucracies?

A. They are technically superior to other forms of organizations.

B. They tend to spread power evenly among those people who are part of them.

C. They can exist only in government, but not in private companies.

D. They tend not to keep any written information concerning their activities, so it is difficult to trace what they have done.

________ **7.** According to Robert Michels, organizations tend to lead to oligarchies because

A. organizations often do not have a strong enough hierarchy of power.

B. people frequently refuse to defer to leaders, causing disruptions in accomplishing goals.

C. those people at the top of the hierarchy have advantages that help them increase their power.

D. those people at the top of the hierarchy do not use coercion often enough to force people to work toward goals.

________ **8.** A bureaucracy is an example of a formal organization because

A. bureaucracies and formal organizations are always run by governments.

B. bureaucracies are deliberately created to reach long-term goals.

C. everyone in the organization has the same amount of power.

D. bureaucracies and formal organizations both tend to last only until a specific goal is met.

________ **9.** A hierarchy of authority

A. should not exist in a bureaucracy.

B. usually exists in informal organizations but is not necessary in formal organizations.

C. is shaped like a pyramid.

D. uses coercion and conflict to force people to follow unwritten rules.

________ **10.** A bureaucracy is based on

A. informal organizations. **C.** coercion.

B. oligarchy. **D.** rationalization.

NAME ________________________ DATE ____________ CLASS ____________

Chapter 6 Test, Form A

networks

Groups and Formal Organizations

DIRECTIONS: Matching Match each item with the correct statement below.

_______ **1.** when individuals or groups combine their efforts to reach a goal	**A.** authority
_______ **2.** groups used for self-evaluation and the formation of values and beliefs	**B.** primary group
_______ **3.** a voluntary action that involves the expectation of a reward	**C.** reference group
_______ **4.** people who are emotionally close and know one another well	**D.** group
_______ **5.** socially approved use of power	**E.** social exchange
_______ **6.** interaction aimed at defeating an opponent	**F.** social network
_______ **7.** consists of at least two people who think, feel, and behave in similar ways	**G.** cooperation
_______ **8.** people who share a social characteristic	**H.** social category
_______ **9.** web of social relationships that join a person to other people	**I.** conflict
_______ **10.** people who happen to be in the same place at the same time	**J.** social aggregate

DIRECTIONS: Multiple Choice Indicate the answer choice that best completes the statement or answers the question.

_______ **11.** One function of a reference group is to

A. exclude others.
B. form identities.
C. eliminate group boundaries.
D. establish relationships.

_______ **12.** Many of the residents of a small town have joined together to create a neighborhood park. This collection of people is an example of a

A. social aggregate.
B. social category.
C. primary group.
D. secondary group.

_______ **13.** A motel manager requires that all maids wear the same uniform or they will be fired. This is an example of

A. cooperation.
B. groupthink.
C. conformity.
D. coercion.

_______ **14.** Which of the following best expresses the idea of conformity?

A. What do you think?
B. I don't think we should go there.
C. But everyone else is doing it!
D. That's a bad idea!

_______ **15.** What is one way the Internet affects a social network?

A. It slows down the flow of information among networks.
B. It establishes boundaries between different networks.
C. It encourages more face-to-face contact.
D. It expands the amount of interaction within networks.

_______ **16.** Which of the following is a characteristic of members of a group?

A. They have at least one interest or goal in common.
B. They do not need to take each other's behavior into account.
C. They avoid conflict.
D. They all have the same social status.

_______ **17.** The idea that power concentrates in fewer and fewer hands is called

A. a bureaucracy.
B. the iron rule of oligarchy.
C. rationalization.
D. a formal organization .

_______ **18.** Primary relationships are more likely to develop if the size of the group is small. What is the main reason for this fact?

A. It is easier to know individuals well when you are in a small group rather than in a large one.
B. Large groups tend to be more coercive.
C. Large groups tend to be more informal and therefore there is a less structured environment in which to get to know people.
D. Large groups tend to meet more often than small groups.

_______ **19.** Which of the following is an example of coercion?

A. Parents ask children to do chores.
B. A group of students ridicules another student.
C. Guards use force against prisoners to make them compliant.
D. An excellent student is rewarded with good grades.

_______ **20.** Which of the following is an advantage of a bureaucracy?

A. increased costs because of extra staff
B. efficiency because of family ties
C. rules promise at least a measure of equal treatment
D. speed of arbitrary decision-making

Groups and Formal Organizations

DIRECTIONS: Essay Answer the following questions.

21. Explain Max Weber's analysis of the nature of bureaucracy.

____

____

____

____

____

22. List examples of contemporary formal organizations and identify the probable goals of each.

____

____

____

____

____

"They raise the possibility that human nature—or more specifically—the kind of character produced in American democratic society, cannot be counted on to insulate its citizens from brutality and inhumane treatment at the direction of malevolent authority. A substantial proportion of people do what they are told to do, irrespective of the content of the act and without limitations of conscience, so long as they perceive that the command comes from a legitimate authority."

—Stanley Milgram, from *Obedience to Authority: An Experimental View,* 1974

23. Researcher Stanley Milgram conducted an experiment that showed how far people are willing to go in order to please a person in authority. Why do you think people are willing to sacrifice their own sense of right and wrong in order to obey an authority figure?

____

____

____

____

____

NAME ______________________ DATE ______________ CLASS __________

Chapter 6 Test, Form B

networks

Groups and Formal Organizations

DIRECTIONS: Matching Match each item with the correct statement below.

________ **1.** exclusive group that demands loyalty from its members		**A.** primary relationship
________ **2.** interaction that is intimate, personal, and caring		**B.** in-group
________ **3.** a group targeted for opposition and antagonism		**C.** secondary group
________ **4.** formal organizations based on rationality and efficiency		**D.** out-group
________ **5.** people who share only part of their lives while focusing on a goal		**E.** bureaucracies
________ **6.** self-deceptive thinking based on conformity to group beliefs		**F.** formal organization
________ **7.** impersonal interaction involving limited parts of personalities		**G.** power
________ **8.** when individuals are forced to behave in a certain way		**H.** coercion
________ **9.** a group created to achieve a long-term goal		**I.** secondary relationship
________ **10.** the ability to control the behavior of others		**J.** groupthink

DIRECTIONS: Multiple Choice Indicate the answer choice that best completes the statement or answers the question.

________ **11.** What happens in the bystander effect?

A. People fail to act because they assume other people will take action.
B. Groups form to watch an action unfold.
C. Members of a group obey the commands of a leader.
D. Individuals act independently of other group members.

________ **12.** What is one characteristic of groups?

A. They are always a small and informal.
B. The members of a group tend to include insiders and outsiders.
C. They do not create boundaries.
D. The include as many people as possible.

________ **13.** Which of the following best describes bureaucracies?

A. They keep written records of their activities.
B. They encourage the promotion of people based on social connections and family relationships.
C. They are informal organizations.
D. They rarely have written rules and procedures.

Chapter 6 Test, Form B *cont.*

Groups and Formal Organizations

_______ **14.** Which of the following best describes how in-groups relate to out-groups?

A. belonging
B. antagonism
C. cooperation
D. loyalty

_______ **15.** Why is continuous contact among its members important for the formation of a primary group?

A. Close relationships among group members often take time to develop.
B. Large primary groups take a long time to form.
C. People need to be able to recognize the weaker members of a primary group.
D. Close contact helps people in a primary group learn to work well together.

_______ **16.** A student reads all about ballet dancers and admires their discipline and hard work. This is an example of a(n)

A. reference group.
B. in-group.
C. out-group.
D. social network.

_______ **17.** Thirty retired people who go on a two-week tour of Europe together are an example of a

A. primary group.
B. secondary group.
C. bureaucracy.
D. social category.

_______ **18.** Marie's best friend lives across the street from her, and the two friends spend most of their free time together. This is an example of a

A. secondary relationship.
B. social aggregate.
C. primary relationship.
D. social category.

_______ **19.** Authority refers to using power

A. to promote conflict.
B. that derives from a legitimate source.
C. to discriminate against specific social categories of people.
D. in an illegal way.

_______ **20.** What occurs when people conform to social pressure and refuse to express their concerns?

A. a social exchange
B. an in-group
C. a conflict
D. groupthink

Chapter 6 Test, Form B *cont.*

Groups and Formal Organizations

DIRECTIONS: Essay Answer the following questions on a separate sheet of paper.

21. Using specific examples, define primary and secondary groups. Contrast their respective functions.

Organization Type	16–24 years	25–34 years	35–44 years	45–54 years	55–64 years	65 and above
Civic & political	5.5	5.5	5.3	8.1	9.3	8.7
Educational & youth	32.4	34.1	39.8	26.0	13.2	6.4
Environment & Animal Care	1.5	2.4	1.4	1.5	2.0	1.4
Hospital & Health	8.6	6.4	5.5	6.9	8.9	10.9
Public Safety	1.7	2.2	1.4	1.4	1.5	1.1
Religious	28.5	30.4	30.5	35.3	39.6	45.2
Social Service	13.0	11.1	9.0	12.3	15.0	16.9
Sport/Hobby	3.4	2.8	3.4	4.2	4.3	3.6
Other*	4.9	5.2	3.8	4.2	6.1	5.9

*includes undetermined

Source: *Statistical Abstract of the United States*

22. This table shows the percentage of the population who participate in volunteer activities, according to age and the type of activity. Contrast the change in membership in educational organizations and in religious organizations as people move from one age group to another. How can you explain the different membership trends in these two organizational groups?

NAME ____________________ DATE ____________________ CLASS __________

Lesson Quiz 7-1

networks

Deviance and Social Control

DIRECTIONS: True/False In the blank, indicate whether the statement is true (T) or false (F).

________ **1.** Deviance is relative to time and place and therefore its definition can change.

________ **2.** Societies and groups frequently use social sanctions to exert external social control.

________ **3.** Positive deviance can be as disruptive as negative deviance.

________ **4.** The process of socialization ensures that all people in society will conform all the time.

________ **5.** Low grades are an example of an informal social sanction.

DIRECTIONS: Multiple Choice Indicate the answer choice that best completes the statement or answers the question.

________ **6.** Social control refers to

A. the folkways practiced by a society.

B. the methods a society uses to promote order and stability.

C. the violation of a social sanction.

D. the rebellious behavior of many adolescents.

________ **7.** Which of the following is an example of a positive social sanction?

A. receiving a promotion at work for completing a project ahead of schedule

B. being required to go to a safe-driving school because you got a speeding ticket

C. having your car insurance premium raised for getting a speeding ticket

D. not being allowed to go out with friends on the weekend because of poor grades

________ **8.** Which of the following is true concerning deviant behavior?

A. Primary deviance usually leads to secondary deviance.

B. What is considered deviant in one society may not be considered deviant in another society.

C. Deviant behavior is also illegal behavior.

D. Adults learn deviant behavior more quickly than children.

________ **9.** How does positive deviance differ from negative deviance?

A. Positive deviance occurs when people over-conform.

B. Society benefits from positive deviance.

C. Negative deviance occurs when people idealize group norms.

D. Positive deviance is easier to manage.

________ **10.** Which of the following is an example of a formal social sanction?

A. bullying someone

B. receiving an award

C. gossiping about someone

D. giving a hand shake

NAME _______________ DATE _______________ CLASS _______________

Lesson Quiz 7-2

networks

Deviance and Social Control

DIRECTIONS: Modified True/False In the blank, indicate whether the statement is true (T) or false (F). If false, edit the statement to make it a true statement.

_______ **1.** Deviance can only affect society in negative ways.

____

_______ **2.** According to strain theory, deviance is more likely when there is a gap between socially approved goals and the means of obtaining them.

____

_______ **3.** One beneficial effect of deviance is that it helps clarify societal norms.

____

_______ **4.** According to control theory, deviance is the consequence of too many social bonds.

____

_______ **5.** Attachment to groups and individuals is one component of a social bond.

____

DIRECTIONS: Multiple Choice Indicate the answer choice that best completes the statement or answers the question.

_______ **6.** It is so important to Chris to appear successful to others that he begins stealing goods from the warehouse where he works and reselling them to obtain money. What is this an example of?

A. ritualism
B. conformity
C. innovation
D. retreatism

_______ **7.** According to control theory, which of the following is important in determining the strength of a person's conformity to social norms?

A. a person's race
B. participation in approved social activities
C. a person's gender
D. the economic status of a person's family

_______ **8.** According to Durkheim, the social condition in which norms are weak, conflicting, or absent is called

A. retreatism.
B. strain.
C. anomie.
D. ritualism.

_______ **9.** Which of the following is a negative effect of deviance?

A. It provides a safety valve.
B. It promotes social change.
C. It causes society to reaffirm norms.
D. It erodes trust.

_______ **10.** When you reject a goal but continue to use socially-accepted means of achieving that goal, you are engaging in

A. conformity.
B. ritualism.
C. retreatism.
D. rebellion.

NAME ______________________________ DATE ____________________ CLASS ____________

Lesson Quiz 7-3

networks

Deviance and Social Control

DIRECTIONS: Matching Match each item with the correct statement below.

______ **1.** theory that explains why deviance is a matter of social definitions

______ **2.** identifies deviant behavior that only occurs as an isolated act

______ **3.** an undesirable label used to deny full social acceptance to a person

______ **4.** term used to describe when deviance becomes a lifestyle

______ **5.** emphasizes the role of primary groups in transmitting deviance

A. stigma

B. differential association theory

C. labeling theory

D. secondary deviance

E. primary deviance

DIRECTIONS: Multiple Choice Indicate the answer choice that best completes the statement or answers the question.

______ **6.** A group whose members use illegal drugs, steal money to pay for their habits, and do not respect the law is engaging in

A. retreatism.
B. primary deviance.
C. secondary deviance.
D. retribution.

______ **7.** Which theory states that deviance is relative and depends on who or what group is defining the deviant behavior?

A. differential association theory
B. strain theory
C. labeling theory
D. control theory

______ **8.** Primary deviance occurs when a person

A. engages only in an isolated act of deviance.
B. adopts a deviant lifestyle.
C. is labeled as a deviant.
D. adopts new norms.

______ **9.** Students in George's sixth-grade class avoid him because they know his father is in prison for auto theft. This is an example of

A. ritualism.
B. rebellion.
C. a stigma.
D. attachment.

______ **10.** Consider the following statement: "The more you hang around with a group of teenagers who shoplift, the more likely it is that you will become a shoplifter." Which of the following theories would most strongly agree with this statement?

A. control theory
B. differential association theory
C. labeling theory
D. retreatism theory

NAME ____________________ DATE ____________ CLASS ________

Lesson Quiz 7-4

networks

Deviance and Social Control

DIRECTIONS: Modified True/False In the blank, indicate whether the statement is true (T) or false (F). If false, edit the statement to make it a true statement.

_______ **1.** Statistics show that the criminal justice system treats members of minority groups more harshly than whites.

____

_______ **2.** Victim discounting occurs when police investigate the same types of crimes more vigorously in upper-class neighborhoods than in lower-class neighborhoods.

____

_______ **3.** White-collar crimes are generally less significant than other forms of crime.

____

_______ **4.** According to Steven Spitzer, one way industrial societies protect themselves is to label their critics deviants.

____

_______ **5.** According to conflict theory, people who have less power in society are also less likely to be convicted of crimes.

____

DIRECTIONS: Multiple Choice Indicate the answer choice that best completes the statement or answers the question.

_______ **6.** A computer operator figures out a way to steal from the bank where he works by sending money to a secret account. This is an example of

A. retreatism.
B. control theory.
C. labeling theory.
D. white-collar crime.

_______ **7.** Which of the following is considered deviant behavior in industrial society?

A. refusal to work
B. owning private property
C. competition among employees
D. agrarian labor

_______ **8.** How are minorities treated differently in the American criminal justice system?

A. They are treated less harshly.
B. They are treated about the same.
C. They are treated more harshly.
D. They are mostly ignored.

_______ **9.** How does victim discounting affect the seriousness of crimes directed at members of lower social classes?

A. It reduces the seriousness.
B. It raises the seriousness.
C. It ignores the seriousness.
D. It expresses the seriousness.

_______ **10.** According to conflict theory, what term best explain(s) the differences in the ways white people and minorities are punished for criminal behavior?

A. anomie
B. labeling
C. level of violence
D. power and resources

NAME ______________________ DATE ____________ CLASS ____________

Lesson Quiz 7-5

networks

Deviance and Social Control

DIRECTIONS: Completion Enter the appropriate word(s) to complete the statement.

1. Any act that violates the law is an example of a ____________.

2. Since 2009, rates of crime in the United States have ____________.

3. A person is in jail for burglary. Two weeks after he is released, he begins burglarizing homes again and is soon back in prison. This is an example of ____________.

4. An attempt to change behavior that will be helpful in finding productive jobs when prisoners are released from prison is called ____________.

5. ____________ is based on the idea that criminals who are not on the street cannot commit crimes.

DIRECTIONS: Multiple Choice Indicate the answer choice that best completes the statement or answers the question.

_______ **6.** What is one advantage attributed to diversion strategy as a way society deals with criminal behavior?

A. Recidivism rates are lower.
B. The offender is not stigmatized.
C. Voters generally support this method of treating offenders.
D. It is more effective than incarceration.

_______ **7.** Which of the following is a crime tracked in the FBI's Uniform Crime Reports?

A. drug possession
B. hate crime
C. tax evasion
D. plagiarism

_______ **8.** Which of the following expresses the current trend in juvenile crime?

A. Crime rates have remained about the same.
B. Crime rates have dropped significantly.
C. Crime rates have risen slightly in the past 10 years.
D. Crime rates have risen sharply in the past 10 years.

_______ **9.** Which of the following is true about capital punishment?

A. Most Americans believe that capital punishment is not a deterrent to murder.
B. Murder rates increase following a decline in the use of the death penalty.
C. Feelings of revenge contribute to American attitudes toward the death penalty.
D. Nearly all countries have capital punishment.

_______ **10.** Which of the following is a method that the criminal justice system uses to control and punish criminals?

A. remuneration of offenders
B. requiring criminals to compensate their victims
C. retreatism
D. victim discounting

NAME ______________________________ DATE ____________________ CLASS ______________

Chapter 7 Test, Form A

networks

Deviance and Social Control

DIRECTIONS: Matching Match each item with the correct statement below.

_______ **1.** explains that strong bonds between individuals and society reinforce social norms

_______ **2.** a person who violates the norms of society

_______ **3.** an undesirable label that may adversely affect a person

_______ **4.** over-conforming to the norms of society

_______ **5.** a state in which norms are weak, conflicting, or absent

_______ **6.** explains why deviance is relative

_______ **7.** rejecting the norms of society

_______ **8.** job-related crimes committed by high-status people

_______ **9.** repetition of criminal behavior

_______ **10.** changing a criminal through socialization

A. control theory

B. white-collar crime

C. deviant

D. anomie

E. stigma

F. negative deviance

G. recidivism

H. labeling theory

I. positive deviance

J. rehabilitation

DIRECTIONS: Multiple Choice Indicate the answer choice that best completes the statement or answers the question.

_______ **11.** What does differential association theory emphasize?

A. The role of primary groups in transmitting deviance.

B. How labels have an effect on deviant behavior.

C. The bonds that exist between individuals and society.

D. The different deviant responses to social strain that occur.

_______ **12.** Which of the following is/are frequently used to exert external social control?

A. retreatism

B. retribution

C. ritualism

D. social sanctions

_______ **13.** Which of the following is considered to be an example of a victimless crime?

A. robbery

B. illegal gambling

C. extortion

D. fraud

_______ **14.** Which of the following may arise from a lack of social norms?

A. anomie

B. ritualism

C. positive deviance

D. stigma

_______ **15.** A plumber has stolen thousands of dollars from individuals by installing substandard plumbing fixtures. The judge says that the plumber must pay for new fixtures for these people's homes. This is an example of

A. ritualism.

B. recidivism.

C. restitution.

D. rehabilitation.

_______ **16.** How does internal social control differ from external social control?

A. Internal social control develops during the socialization process.

B. Internal social control involves formal sanctions.

C. Most internal social control takes place outside the individual.

D. Internal social control provides less stability than external social control.

_______ **17.** A person enters a social hall and finds a box that contains donations people have made to feed the poor. Because he considers himself to be poor, he takes money from the box. Which of the following terms best describes this person's behavior?

A. innovation

B. rebellion

C. ritualism

D. retreatism

_______ **18.** Which of the following is an example of white-collar crime?

A. drunk driving

B. tax evasion

C. shoplifting

D. plagiarism

_______ **19.** How does primary deviance differ from secondary deviance?

A. Primary deviance derives from primary groups.

B. Secondary deviance is not as important as primary deviance.

C. In primary deviance people identify with deviant behavior.

D. Primary deviance is deviant behavior that only happens once in a while.

_______ **20.** Which of the following is true about deviance?

A. Deviance can only affect society in negative ways.

B. Some societies have eliminated deviance altogether.

C. It is easy to identify deviant behavior.

D. Ideas of deviance can change from one social context to another.

DIRECTIONS: Essay Answer the following questions.

21. In what ways can deviant behavior promote social change? Use examples in your answer.

____

____

____

____

____

22. Identify and describe primary and secondary degrees of deviance.

____

____

____

____

____

____

TWO TYPES OF YOUTH DEVIANCE	1995	1997	1999	2001	2003	2005	2007	2009	2011
Carried a weapon	20.0	18.3	17.3	17.4	17.1	18.5	18.0	17.5	16.6
Was in a physical fight	38.7	36.6	35.7	33.2	33.0	35.9	35.5	31.5	32.8

Source: "Trends in the Prevalence of Behaviors that Contribute to Violence," Centers for Disease Control and Prevention, 2012.

23. The chart above shows trends in two types of youth deviance. What overall trend do you observe? What do you think explains the fact that the trend for both types of deviance does not occur in a straight line? In what way can youth deviance be considered an example of primary deviance?

____

____

____

____

____

____

NAME ______________________ DATE ______________ CLASS __________

Chapter 7 Test, Form B

networks

Deviance and Social Control

DIRECTIONS: Matching Match each item with the correct statement below.

______ **1.** people go through the motions without believing in the process		**A.** deterrence
______ **2.** ways to encourage conformity to societal norms		**B.** victim discounting
______ **3.** people reject the means and the goals of society		**C.** social control
______ **4.** behavior that departs from societal and group norms		**D.** secondary deviance
______ **5.** reducing the seriousness of crimes against people of lower status		**E.** ritualism
______ **6.** rewards or punishments that encourage conformity		**F.** primary deviance
______ **7.** an act committed in violation of the law		**G.** social sanctions
______ **8.** discouraging criminal acts by threats of punishment		**H.** retreatism
______ **9.** when deviance becomes a lifestyle		**I.** crime
______ **10.** only occasional breaking of norms		**J.** deviance

DIRECTIONS: Multiple Choice Indicate the answer choice that best completes the statement or answers the question.

______ **11.** Why is social control important?

A. It establishes nonconformity.

B. It creates stability.

C. It promotes unpredictability.

D. It generates deviance.

______ **12.** A young high-school dropout is sent to prison for repeated car theft. While in prison, the individual is helped to obtain his high-school equivalency diploma. This increases his chances of getting a good job when he is released, and is an example of

A. recidivism.

B. rehabilitation.

C. rebellion.

D. ritualism.

______ **13.** Which of the following is an example of an informal social sanction?

A. school awards

B. detention

C. gossip

D. expulsion

Chapter 7 Test, Form B *cont.*

Deviance and Social Control

_______ **14.** The police and judicial courts are both part of

A. the criminal justice system.

B. control theory.

C. recidivism.

D. retreatism.

_______ **15.** Even though Stephan studied hard during the first semester of chemistry class, he still received a D. During the second semester, he decided it was hopeless and quit studying. Which of the following best describes his behavior?

A. innovation

B. rebellion

C. ritualism

D. retreatism

_______ **16.** Which of the following words can be considered an example of a stigma?

A. cheater

B. hero

C. doctor

D. studious

_______ **17.** Which of the following best describes a person who exhibits positive deviance?

A. a criminal

B. a perfectionist

C. an outsider

D. a nonconformist

_______ **18.** Which of the following would be considered socially-acceptable in an industrial society?

A. threatening private property

B. adopting a policy that prohibits promotions

C. competing for a higher paying job

D. refusing to participate in the work process

_______ **19.** Which of the following is a deviant response to strain?

A. imagination

B. deterrence

C. retreatism

D. anomie

_______ **20.** What does labeling theory help us understand?

A. how socialization helps transmit deviance

B. how deviant behavior is a matter of social definition

C. how society can control deviance through sanctions

D. how primary and secondary deviance differ

Chapter 7 Test, Form B *cont.*

Deviance and Social Control

DIRECTIONS: Essay Answer the following questions.

21. Of the four approaches to crime control—deterrence, retribution, incarceration, and rehabilitation—explain which one you feel may be least effective in reducing the crime rate. Support your response with examples and evidence.

"... Townspeople never perceived the Saints' high level of delinquency. The Saints were good boys who just went in for an occasional prank. After all, they were well dressed, well mannered and had nice cars. The Roughnecks (another gang at the same high school) were a different story. Although the two gangs of boys were the same age, and both groups engaged in an equal amount of wild-oat sowing, everyone agreed that the-not-so-well-dressed, not-so-well-mannered, not-so-rich boys were heading for trouble ..."

—from William J. Chambliss, "The Saints and the Roughnecks," *Society* 11, November/December 1973

Credit: *The Saints and the Roughnecks* by William J. Chambliss. Used by permission of the author.

22. How does this quote illustrate society's attitude toward deviant behavior?

NAME ______________________ DATE ______________ CLASS ____________

Lesson Quiz 8-1

networks

Social Stratification

DIRECTIONS: True/False In the blank, indicate whether the statement is true (T) or false (F).

_______ **1.** A person who has power will also have prestige.

_______ **2.** Each layer in a stratification system is a social class.

_______ **3.** When Karl Marx spoke of false consciousness, he was referring to the working class's acceptance of capitalist ideas.

_______ **4.** Individuals and groups are able to use power only when others allow them to do so.

_______ **5.** According to symbolic interactionism, a person's self-concept helps preserve the existing stratification structure.

DIRECTIONS: Multiple Choice Indicate the answer choice that best completes the statement or answers the question.

_______ **6.** A position such as being a high-school teacher is likely to have more prestige than

A. money.
B. power.
C. status.
D. wealth.

_______ **7.** Which of the following best describes the functionalist theory of social stratification?

A. Inequality exists because some people are willing to exploit others.
B. Social stratification will eventually be eliminated when the workers revolt.
C. Children in the United States.are taught that a person's social class is the result of his or her talent and effort.
D. The inequality of social classes helps assure that the most qualified people fill the most important positions.

_______ **8.** Karl Marx believed that the only thing of value that the proletariat had was

A. the means of production.
B. prestige because of the work it performed.
C. its property.
D. its labor.

_______ **9.** Which of the following best describes how social class is related to social stratification?

A. Each social class has many layers of social stratification.
B. Each layer of social stratification constitutes a social class.
C. The terms social stratification and social class mean the same thing.
D. Social stratification exists in caste systems, whereas social classes exist only in noncaste systems.

_______ **10.** According to conflict theory, social stratification exists because

A. some people are willing to exploit others.
B. self esteem is higher among the upper class.
C. certain jobs are more important than others.
D. different occupations have different levels of prestige.

NAME ________________________ DATE ______________ CLASS __________

Lesson Quiz 8-2

networks

Social Stratification

DIRECTIONS: Matching Match each item with the correct statement below.

______ **1.** a small, elite group based on heritage rather than accomplishment

______ **2.** a large segment of society, composed of hourly workers whose income is somewhat below average

______ **3.** people who work at low-skill jobs and have an income below the poverty line

______ **4.** people who are poor, unemployed, and frequently come from families that have a history of not working regularly

______ **5.** a fairly large group of people with professions that range from upper level managers and professionals to non-retail salespeople

A. underclass

B. middle class

C. working poor

D. working class

E. aristocracy

DIRECTIONS: Multiple Choice Indicate the answer choice that best completes the statement or answers the question.

______ **6.** Which of the following is least likely to live in poverty in the United States today?

A. a 30-year-old white man

B. an African American mother of two preschoolers

C. a 14-year-old Latino boy

D. a mentally ill 45-year-old white woman

______ **7.** How is poverty measured in the United States?

A. by sending out surveys to all American families

B. by conducting interviews with people in the underclass

C. by setting an annual base level income for a family of four

D. by measuring annual levels of unemployment

______ **8.** Which of the following describes rates of poverty for African Americans and Latinos?

A. lower than rates for whites

B. about the same as rates for whites

C. slightly higher than rates for whites

D. much higher than rates for whites

______ **9.** Which of the following best explains why women have a higher risk of being poor?

A. Corporate employers are reluctant to hire women.

B. Many women choose not to use child-care facilities.

C. Women earn about 80 cents for every dollar earned by men.

D. Most women choose professions that pay less.

______ **10.** Which of the following best describes how Americans regard class consciousness?

A. very significant to American identity

B. less important than other markers of identity

C. not relevant to American identity

D. as part of the principle of equality

NAME ______________________ DATE ______________ CLASS __________

Lesson Quiz 8-3

networks

Social Stratification

DIRECTIONS: Completion Enter the appropriate word(s) to complete the statement.

1. Social mobility is defined as the ability to move between social ____________.

2. In a caste system, people acquire social status by ____________ it.

3. A factory worker's daughter works her way through college and eventually becomes a sociology professor. This is an example of ____________.

4. In the United States, manufacturing jobs became more available after World War II . This availability increased upward ____________.

5. In an open-class system, social class is based on ____________ and individual effort.

DIRECTIONS: Multiple Choice Indicate the answer choice that best completes the statement or answers the question.

_______ **6.** Which of the following is an example of intergenerational mobility?

A. a restaurant server becomes a bus driver
B. a lawyer becomes a surgeon
C. a surgeon's son becomes a lawyer
D. a corporate vice president becomes a chef

_______ **7.** Which of the following is true about a caste system?

A. A caste system is a closed-class system.
B. Members of different castes are allowed to marry.
C. Social class is earned.
D. Mobility can be achieved through merit.

_______ **8.** What is one reason that many Americans today risk downward mobility?

A. an increase in manufacturing jobs
B. the globalization of business
C. a decrease in the willingness to work
D. overpopulation

_______ **9.** How does horizontal mobility differ from vertical mobility?

A. Horizontal mobility does not involve a change in class.
B. Only horizontal mobility involves a change of occupation.
C. People change classes in horizontal mobility.
D. Horizontal mobility occurs between generations.

_______ **10.** Which of the following best characterizes an open-class system?

A. a safety net for all
B. survival of the fittest
C. a chicken in every pot
D. from rags to riches

NAME ______________________________ DATE ____________________ CLASS ____________

Lesson Quiz 8-4

networks

Social Stratification

DIRECTIONS: True/False In the blank, indicate whether the statement is true (T) or false (F).

________ **1.** Global stratification refers to the unequal distribution of wealth, power, and resources among countries.

________ **2.** Cambodia, Afghanistan, and Somalia are examples of middle-income countries.

________ **3.** One effect of globalization is that it may limit the economic development of poor nations.

________ **4.** The process of industrialization has prevented many low-income countries from developing a higher level of income.

________ **5.** Rates of infant mortality, access to clean water, and life expectancy are indicators that are often used to measure poverty.

DIRECTIONS: Multiple Choice Indicate the answer choice that best completes the statement or answers the question.

________ **6.** What is one reason that industrialization enables nations to develop?

A. Fewer people work in agrarian contexts.

B. Science, technology, and learning develop more rapidly.

C. More people own the means of production.

D. Levels of urbanization decrease.

________ **7.** Which of the following is characteristic of middle-income nations?

A. The standard of living is about the same for all of the countries.

B. Income levels vary greatly among them.

C. Examples include France, Japan, and Abu Dhabi.

D. They make up about twenty percent of the world's countries.

________ **8.** Some sociologists believe that many poor nations are poor because

A. they have cut ties to their former colonizers.

B. people in the nation do not work hard enough.

C. powerful nations took control of their resources.

D. they have not yet joined the process of globalization.

________ **9.** Which of the following is characteristic of low-income nations?

A. access to clean water

B. high levels of literacy

C. decreased life expectancy

D. industrialization

________ **10.** One criticism of globalization is that it

A. exploits the conditions of poor nations.

B. leads to increased urbanization.

C. continues the process of industrialization.

D. excludes some nations from the global economy.

Chapter 8 Test, Form A

networks

Social Stratification

DIRECTIONS: Matching Match each item with the correct statement below.

_______ **1.** each layer in a stratification system

_______ **2.** change in class that takes place over a generation

_______ **3.** the state in which one is unable to secure life's necessities

_______ **4.** movement from an economy based on agriculture to one based on manufacturing

_______ **5.** the group that owns the means of production

_______ **6.** measure of poverty by economic disparity

_______ **7.** changing from one social class to another

_______ **8.** group that labors without ownership

_______ **9.** changing occupations within the same class

_______ **10.** development of an increasingly integrated world economy

A. horizontal mobility

B. proletariat

C. vertical mobility

D. bourgeoisie

E. intergenerational mobility

F. relative poverty

G. social class

H. absolute poverty

I. globalization

J. industrialization

DIRECTIONS: Multiple Choice Indicate the answer choice that best completes the statement or answers the question.

_______ **11.** Which of the following people would most likely be a member of the working poor?

A. a man with few marketable skills who comes from a family in which people typically worked only enough to get by

B. a single woman with a college degree

C. a husband and wife who both have technology-related skills

D. a skilled carpenter with a wife and two children

_______ **12.** When you add up all the economic resources a person has, such as her savings, home, personal property, etc., you have determined that person's

A. caste.

B. power.

C. wealth.

D. prestige.

_______ **13.** Irina moves from a job as a computer programmer to a job as a Webpage designer. This is most likely an example of

A. intergenerational mobility.

B. horizontal mobility.

C. vertical mobility.

D. the caste system.

______ **14.** Which of the following refers to the different layers of people who possess varying amounts of scarce resources?

A. the proletariat
B. class consciousness
C. social stratification
D. horizontal mobility

______ **15.** People who do not earn enough money to pay for a safe place to live and for food

A. live in absolute poverty.
B. live in relative poverty.
C. are members of the working class in the United States.
D. belong to the aristocracy.

______ **16.** A skilled plumber would most likely be a member of the

A. lower-upper class.
B. working poor.
C. working class.
D. underclass.

______ **17.** What occurs when an agrarian society experiences industrialization?

A. Urbanization increases.
B. Less food is needed to support the population of workers.
C. People move away from cities.
D. The need for energy sources decreases.

______ **18.** Which of the following is an indicator that is used to measure poverty?

A. race
B. infant mortality rate
C. access to green space
D. religious affiliation

______ **19.** Which of the following statements is true of prestige?

A. Prestige must be claimed for oneself.
B. Only the working class is interested in obtaining prestige.
C. Only the bourgeoisie is able to obtain prestige.
D. What might be considered prestigious by one social class may not be considered prestigious by another.

______ **20.** Which of the following is true of middle-income nations?

A. Most countries in the world are middle-income.
B. Living standards among these countries vary greatly.
C. About ten percent of the world's poor live in them.
D. Canada, Germany, and Japan are middle-income countries.

Social Stratification

DIRECTIONS: Essay Answer the following questions.

21. Analyze the belief by many sociologists that upward vertical social mobility is not a possibility for many members of American society.

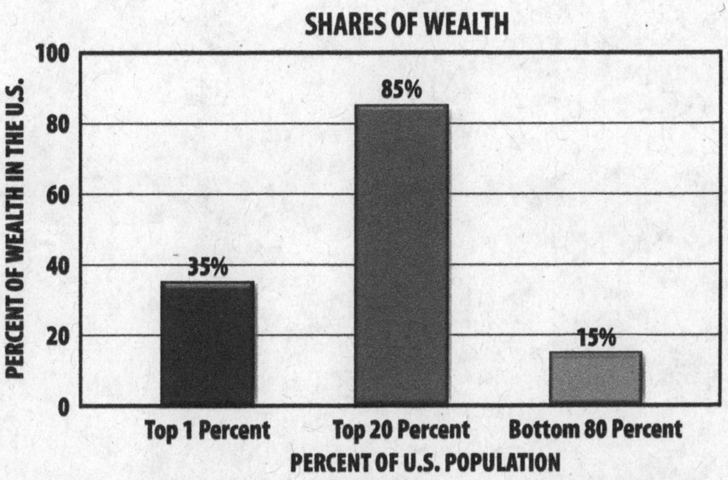

Source: Edward N. Wolff, "Recent Trends in Household Wealth in the United States: Rising Debt and the Middle Class Squeeze–an Update to 2007," Working Paper No. 589. The Levy Economics Institute, March 2010.

22. This graph shows the distribution of wealth in the United States. What three economic strata does the graph compare? How is the wealth distributed? How is wealth related to income? What would you think is the relationship between income and the data shown in the graph? Why do the percentages in the graph add up to more than 100 percent?

Chapter 8 Test, Form A cont.

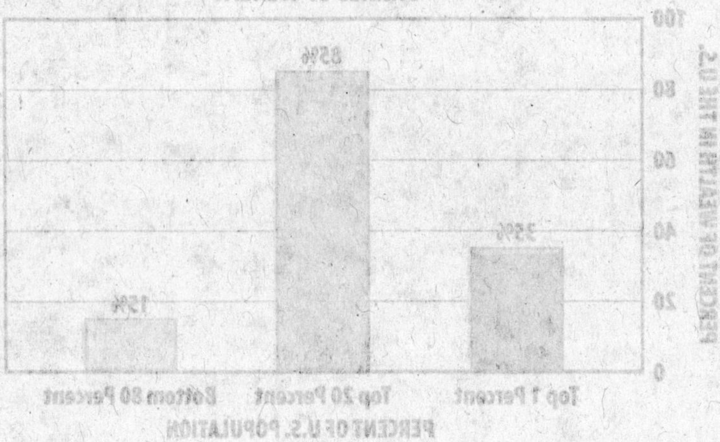

NAME ______________________ DATE ______________ CLASS __________

Chapter 8 Test, Form B

networks

Social Stratification

DIRECTIONS: Matching Match each item with the correct statement below.

______ **1.** a structure in which social class is inherited and there is no social mobility	**A.** false consciousness
______ **2.** identifying with the goals and interests of a particular class	**B.** caste system
______ **3.** the ability to control the behavior of others	**C.** class consciousness
______ **4.** a trend in which women and children are more likely to be poor	**D.** power
______ **5.** a recession causes a worker to accept a lower-paying job	**E.** open-class system
______ **6.** when the working class accepts capitalist values	**F.** standard of living
______ **7.** the unequal distribution of wealth among countries	**G.** prestige
______ **8.** the level of necessities and comforts available to people in a society	**H.** feminization of poverty
______ **9.** a structure in which social class is based on individual achievement	**I.** downward mobility
______ **10.** recognition and respect attached to social positions	**J.** global stratification

DIRECTIONS: Multiple Choice Indicate the answer choice that best completes the statement or answers the question.

______ **11.** To which social class do most Americans think they belong?

A. upper-upper class
B. lower-upper class
C. middle class
D. working class

______ **12.** Which of the following is true of low-income nations?

A. They are often industrialized.
B. Rates of literacy are sometimes high.
C. They have higher rates of infant mortality.
D. Brazil, Korea, and Iran are examples.

______ **13.** What word best describes the amount of money a person earns within a specific time period?

A. wealth
B. stratification
C. income
D. prestige

______ **14.** A disabled 56-year-old man with no source of income other than disability payments from the federal government most likely belongs to the

A. middle class.
B. lower-upper class.
C. working poor.
D. underclass.

______ **15.** The most distinguishing characteristic of a caste system is that

A. people's social class can change vertically but not horizontally.
B. people can only change from one generation to the next.
C. social status is inherited and cannot be changed.
D. social status can be changed by education and hard work.

______ **16.** After attending night school for five years, Sondra moves from a job as a warehouse worker to a job as a bank executive. This is most likely an example of

A. intergenerational mobility.
B. horizontal mobility.
C. vertical mobility.
D. the caste system.

______ **17.** Which of the following best describes what Karl Marx meant by *false consciousness*?

A. the working class's acceptance of capitalist ideas
B. the social class into which you are born is the one you should remain in your entire life
C. most of the people in industrial societies belong to the middle class
D. social stratification increases the stability of a society

______ **18.** Which of the following is a consequence of industrialization?

A. An intellectual class of laborers developed.
B. Literacy and formal education decreased.
C. Industrial societies brought lower levels of social inequality.
D. The population of cities steadily decreased.

______ **19.** A major characteristic of the aristocracy is that

A. their social status depends on their profession.
B. minorities such as African Americans and Latinos make up a large segment.
C. the current generation has had to work hard and show great skill to create their wealth.
D. they have been wealthy for many generations.

______ **20.** Which of the following would be considered part of a person's wealth?

A. her tax forms
B. her clothes and other personal possessions
C. a paycheck she will receive next Friday
D. a house that she rents

Social Stratification

DIRECTIONS: Essay Answer the following questions.

21. What are two major characteristics of American social class structures? Include statistics and descriptions of each social class in your response.

____

____

____

____

____

22. What are some characteristics that identify the poor in America?

____

____

____

____

____

"What these tests tell employers about potential employees is hard to imagine since the 'right' answers should be obvious to anyone who has encountered the principle of hierarchy and subordination. ... The real function of these tests, I decide, is to convey information not to the employer but to the potential employee, and the information being conveyed is always: You will have no secrets from us. We don't just want your muscles and that portion of your brain that is directly connected to them, we want your innermost self."

—from *Nickel and Dimed on (Not) Getting By in America*, by Barbara Ehrenreich, 2011

23. To write her book, Barbara Ehrenreich did research by working at various low-paying jobs in different places in America. This excerpt tells the reader how she feels about the tests she took to secure her positions. How would Karl Marx have viewed her work? What do you think the Ehrenreich means by the phrase "we want your innermost self"?

____

____

____

____

NAME _______________ DATE _______________ CLASS _______________

networks

Lesson Quiz 9-1

Inequalities of Race and Ethnicity

DIRECTIONS: True/False In the blank, indicate whether the statement is true (T) or false (F).

_______ **1.** People who are blind are members of an ethnic minority.

_______ **2.** The more ethnocentric a person is, the more likely he or she is to feel prejudice against others.

_______ **3.** Racial categories are rooted in biology.

_______ **4.** A racial minority often holds an unequal share of society's privileges.

_______ **5.** There is no evidence that some races are innately more intelligent than others.

DIRECTIONS: Multiple Choice Indicate the answer choice that best completes the statement or answers the question.

_______ **6.** Which kind of minority is typically defined by physical characteristics.

A. ethnic
B. assimilated
C. stereotyped
D. racial

_______ **7.** An important characteristic of a minority is that

A. its members must all be of the same race.
B. it is dominated by the majority.
C. members of the minority group must not have any sense of identity.
D. people can choose the minority group to which they wish to belong.

_______ **8.** How does an ethnic minority differ from a race?

A. Physical characteristics define ethnic minorities.
B. Race involves innate cultural differences.
C. Genetics plays a role in an ethnic minority.
D. Cultural differences define ethnic minorities.

_______ **9.** Ethnocentrism often involves

A. negative attitudes toward ethnic minorities.
B. acceptance of ethnic minorities by a majority.
C. greater understanding of social norms.
D. feelings of superiority on the part of ethnic minorities

_______ **10.** Which of the following is characteristic of the relationship between minority and majority groups?

A. Members of the majority have greater access to goods and services.
B. Members of the minority often regard traits of the majority as inferior.
C. Only majorities think in terms of "we" and "they."
D. Members of the minority tend to control the flow of resources.

NAME ______________________________ DATE ______________ CLASS __________

Lesson Quiz 9-2

networks

Inequalities of Race and Ethnicity

DIRECTIONS: Matching Match each item with the correct statement below.

______ **1.** the movement of Native Americans to reservations

______ **2.** a minority group maintains its own culturally unique way of life and does not become part of the larger culture

______ **3.** systematic effort to destroy an entire population

______ **4.** process designed to prevent a minority from achieving equality

______ **5.** the blending of a minority into the dominant society

A. genocide

B. subjugation

C. population transfer

D. accommodation

E. assimilation

DIRECTIONS: Multiple Choice Indicate the answer choice that best completes the statement or answers the question.

______ **6.** The term *Anglo* refers to an American

A. who is part of the middle class.

B. whose ancestors came from anywhere in Europe.

C. whose ancestors came from England.

D. whose ancestors were Catholic.

______ **7.** Which of the following groups is an example of the accommodation pattern of assimilation?

A. African Americans

B. Latino Americans

C. Native Americans

D. the Amish

______ **8.** Which of the following was the primary pattern used by the majority to deal with African Americans who came to the United States as enslaved persons?

A. assimilation

B. genocide

C. accommodation

D. subjugation

______ **9.** When minority groups enter the United States today, they are typically either assimilated or

A. subjugated.

B. conformed.

C. rejected.

D. accommodated.

______ **10.** Which of the following phrases is used to describe forced population transfer?

A. pattern of conflict

B. ethnic cleansing

C. melting pot

D. *de facto* segregation

NAME ______________________ DATE ______________ CLASS __________

Lesson Quiz 9-3

networks

Inequalities of Race and Ethnicity

DIRECTIONS: True/False In the blank, indicate whether the statement is true (T) or false (F).

_______ **1.** People often discriminate against others based on race, but rarely discriminate based on religion.

_______ **2.** Conflict theory states that the majority uses prejudice and discrimination to control a minority.

_______ **3.** Stereotypes can be used to justify unethical treatment of minority groups.

_______ **4.** Hate crimes only involve bias related to race.

_______ **5.** Sociologists define prejudice as widely held negative attitudes toward a group.

DIRECTIONS: Multiple Choice Indicate the answer choice that best completes the statement or answers the question.

_______ **6.** Regarding forms of prejudice, symbolic interactionism states that

A. prejudices weaken the majority group's self-concept.

B. hate crimes are rare among people who are strongly ethnocentric.

C. the majority encourages minorities to assimilate in order to increase the stability of a society.

D. hate crimes always involve demeaning labels that justify violence.

_______ **7.** Manuel was always on the honor roll in high school, so when he went to college he expected to do well in his courses. His grades for the first semester were very good, about the same as those he received in high school. Which of the following best describes this situation?

A. subjugation

B. prejudice

C. stereotyping

D. self-fulfilling prophecy

_______ **8.** Which of the following is an example of a hate crime?

A. a person stealing money from an Asian American because the thief wants to buy drugs

B. painting a swastika on a Jewish neighbor's garage

C. arguing with someone about politics

D. not hiring a Latino American for a job because she does not have the required skills

_______ **9.** Abraham's parents taught him that all white southerners believe that African Americans are inferior to whites. This is an example of

A. a prejudice.

B. a self-fulfilling prophecy.

C. institutionalized discrimination.

D. subjugation.

_______ **10.** Which of the following best describes the functionalist perspective of prejudice and discrimination?

A. When minorities are exploited, the self-concept of the dominant society is weakened.

B. Discrimination improves the economy of the society because minority members will work for low pay.

C. Children learn to sort people into groups by examining the behavior of the adults around them.

D. Because the dominant group feels superior to the minority, its members' self-concepts are strengthened.

Lesson Quiz 9-4

networks

Inequalities of Race and Ethnicity

DIRECTIONS: Completion Write the word or phrase that correctly completes each statement.

1. One barrier to full acceptance in American society faced by African Americans is ______________.

2. Unfair practices that are part of the structure of a society are ______________.

3. The largest minority group in the United States today is______________.

4. The minority, that perhaps more than any other minority, that are suffering today from hundreds of years of discrimination are ______________.

5. A high-school graduate works 30 hours a week stocking groceries at a local supermarket. After looking for full-time work for over a year, he has given up. Because he is no longer seeking a job, the government does not count him as looking for employment. This is an example of __________.

DIRECTIONS: Multiple Choice Indicate the answer choice that best completes the statement or answers the question.

________ 6. Which of the following is an example of institutionalized discrimination?

A. A country will not allow noncitizens to own property.

B. A company tests all job applicants to make certain they can read and write, a necessary requirement for the job.

C. A department manager gives preferential treatment to employees who are his friends, even though this is against company policy.

D. A preschool divides students into classes based on their ages.

________ 7. What is one advance African Americans have made in recent years?

A. Most African Americans now work in professional occupations.

B. Upward mobility has resulted in the growth of a black underclass.

C. African Americans are now fully represented in the United States Senate.

D. Business ownership among African American has increased dramatically.

________ 8. Why did some Americans want to prevent Chinese from immigrating to the United States in the late nineteenth century?

A. They wanted to protect them from discrimination.

B. They feared the spread of new diseases.

C. They wanted to eliminate Chinese competition in the workforce.

D. They worried about the effects of overpopulation.

________ 9. Which ethnic group was interned by the United States government during wartime?

A. Japanese Americans

B. African Americans

C. Native Americans

D. Chinese Americans

________ 10. What group of African Americans suffers from the greatest disparity in unemployment rates when compared to white Americans?

A. African American teenagers

B. African American college graduates

C. African American women

D. Elderly African Americans

Chapter 9 Test, Form A

networks

Inequalities of Race and Ethnicity

DIRECTIONS: Matching Match each item with the correct statement below.

_______ **1.** a metaphor used to describe assimilation

_______ **2.** process by which expectations become reality

_______ **3.** people sharing inherited physical characteristics

_______ **4.** unfair practices that are part of the structure of a society

_______ **5.** a form of subjugation based on law

_______ **6.** an attempt to destroy, in whole or in part, a population

_______ **7.** people differentiated from the dominant group in society

_______ **8.** a minority group is denied equal access to social benefits

_______ **9.** a form of subjugation that happens outside the law

_______ **10.** an illegal act motivated by extreme prejudice

A. subjugation

B. race

C. melting pot

D. minority

E. genocide

F. *de jure* segregation

G. hate crime

H. self-fulfilling prophecy

I. *de facto* segregation

J. institutionalized discrimination

DIRECTIONS: Multiple Choice Indicate the answer choice that best completes the statement or answers the question.

_______ **11.** Which of the following is a pattern of conflict?

A. population transfer

B. assimilation

C. race relations

D. ethnic diversity

_______ **12.** Jews in the United States are members of

A. an ethnic majority.

B. a racial minority.

C. an ethnic minority.

D. the racial majority.

_______ **13.** People who are racist

A. are always members of the majority.

B. believe their race is superior.

C. believe that the dominant race is superior.

D. know that their beliefs are wrong, but are unwilling to change.

_______ **14.** Which of the following best describes the symbolic interactionist view of prejudice?

A. Prejudice allows people's self-concept to be strengthened because they believe they are superior to others.

B. Children are taught to be prejudiced by watching the behavior of significant others who express prejudices.

C. Prejudice strengthens society both economically and culturally.

D. Prejudice only becomes a problem in society when it is institutionalized.

_______ **15.** Which of the following is the most prevalent pattern of assimilation in the United States?

A. accommodation

B. Anglo-conformity

C. melting pot

D. cultural pluralism

_______ **16.** Which of the following is the fastest growing minority group in the United States?

A. African American

B. Asian American

C. Latino

D. Native American

_______ **17.** Which of the following patterns of assimilation occurred most commonly amongst German immigrants to the United States in the early 1900s?

A. accommodation

B. Anglo-assimilation

C. population transfer

D. subjugation

_______ **18.** Which of the following is part of the definition of an ethnic minority?

A. skin color

B. birthplace

C. schooling

D. language

_______ **19.** Accommodation occurs when a minority

A. is forcibly removed from the territory of the dominant culture.

B. severs all ties with the dominant culture.

C. is fully absorbed into the culture of the dominant society.

D. maintains its own culturally unique way of life.

_______ **20.** Historically, many African Americans in southern states were denied the right to vote by government officials who treated them differently from whites; for example, by requiring them to pass complex exams to be able to vote. This is an example of

A. institutionalized discrimination.

B. genocide.

C. ethnocentrism.

D. a self-fulfilling prophecy.

DIRECTIONS: Essay Answer the following questions on a separate sheet of paper.

21. In a relatively few years, projections indicate that American society will have a non-white majority. What implications, if any, do you think this will have on the relations between the races and various ethnic groups?

22. Distinguish between prejudice, racism, and discrimination; discuss examples of each.

23.

"The students did not resolve the tensions and contradictions of second-generation Mexican American women. They saw themselves as Americans when others stereotyped them as foreigners. They saw themselves as foreigners when with Mexican-born family and friends who, in turn, saw them as Americanized Mexicans. As women, they defined themselves as independent and equal when their fathers exerted patriarchal authority over them. In sum, an unfolding process of constructing emergent identities and negotiated spaces shaped their lives."

—from Alma García, *Narratives of Mexican American Women*, 2004

This quote from the work of Alma García reveals ways three Mexican American women view themselves in different contexts. How do the women see themselves? Briefly explain how context can alter one's perceptions of oneself.

NAME ______________________ DATE ______________ CLASS ____________

Chapter 9 Test, Form B

networks

Inequalities of Race and Ethnicity

DIRECTIONS: Matching Match each item with the correct statement below.

_______ **1.** minority

_______ **2.** racism

_______ **3.** population transfer

_______ **4.** ethnic minority

_______ **5.** cultural pluralism

_______ **6.** ethnic cleansing

_______ **7.** genocide

_______ **8.** stereotyping

_______ **9.** assimilation

_______ **10.** ethnocentrism

A. the blending of a minority group into the dominant society

B. a minority group maintains a sense of identity apart from the dominant group

C. the forced removal of an ethnic group from an area.

D. labeling of a group based on distorted or oversimplified images

E. widely held negative attitudes toward a group

F. a minority is forced to leave territory controlled by a majority

G. judging others in terms of one's own cultural standards

H. a group of people who find themselves objects of discrimination

I. a group identified by religious, cultural, or national characteristics

J. the systematic effort to destroy an entire population

DIRECTIONS: Multiple Choice Indicate the answer choice that best completes the statement or answers the question.

_______ **11.** *De jure* segregation differs from *de facto* segregation because it

A. is based on the law.

B. is based on societal practice, not law.

C. has been declared illegal.

D. does not involve discrimination.

_______ **12.** Which of the following is a feature of a majority?

A. shared beliefs or characteristics

B. innate physical advantages

C. prejudice

D. domination by a minority

_______ **13.** Which of the following statements is true concerning African Americans?

A. While their income increases as they receive more education, it increases at a lower rate than that of whites.

B. African Americans' income increases more rapidly than that of whites as they become better educated.

C. Generally speaking, they are discriminated against less than Asian Americans.

D. Their political power has decreased over the past 40 years.

_______ **14.** What is the difference between prejudice and discrimination?

A. Prejudice is an opinion, not an act.

B. Stereotypes occur only in discrimination.

C. Discrimination is a set of values.

D. Prejudice can be positive.

_______ **15.** Urh's family immigrated from Laos thirty years ago when Urh was five years old. While Urh's parents still cook and eat mostly Laotian food, Urh and his wife, who is a native-born American, primarily eat "American" food. In addition, they do not celebrate Laotian holidays unless they are with Urh's parents, but they do celebrate holidays such as Thanksgiving, Christmas, and the Fourth of July. Which of the following terms best describes Urh's orientation?

A. Anglo-assimilation

B. genocide

C. subjugation

D. accommodation

_______ **16.** People who believe in biological determinism think that

A. there are no differences in people based on gender.

B. physical differences produce behavioral differences.

C. biology determines rules that govern society.

D. women value appearance more than men do.

_______ **17.** Which of the following is the most extreme form of conflict?

A. genocide

B. segregation

C. subjugation

D. population transfer

_______ **18.** Which of the following is true of race?

A. Racial categories are biologically determined.

B. Some races have innate advantages over others.

C. Racial differences play a significant role in genetics.

D. There is no scientific evidence for distinct human races.

_______ **19.** Steve tells his friend Tom that he should go out for track because Tom is African American and Steve believes African Americans can run faster than people of other races. This is an example of

A. discrimination.

B. ethnocentrism.

C. subjugation.

D. a stereotype.

_______ **20.** Which of the following is true about Latinos in the United States?

A. Median income among Latino families is about the same as that of whites.

B. Mexican Americans have the highest education attainment level among Latinos.

C. There is little cultural diversity among Latinos living in the United States.

D. Latinos have overtaken African Americans as America's largest minority group.

DIRECTIONS: Essay Answer the following questions on a separate sheet of paper.

21. **MEDIAN FAMILY INCOME FOR MAJORITY AND MINORITY GROUPS, 1990 AND 2009 (CONSTANT 2009 DOLLARS)**

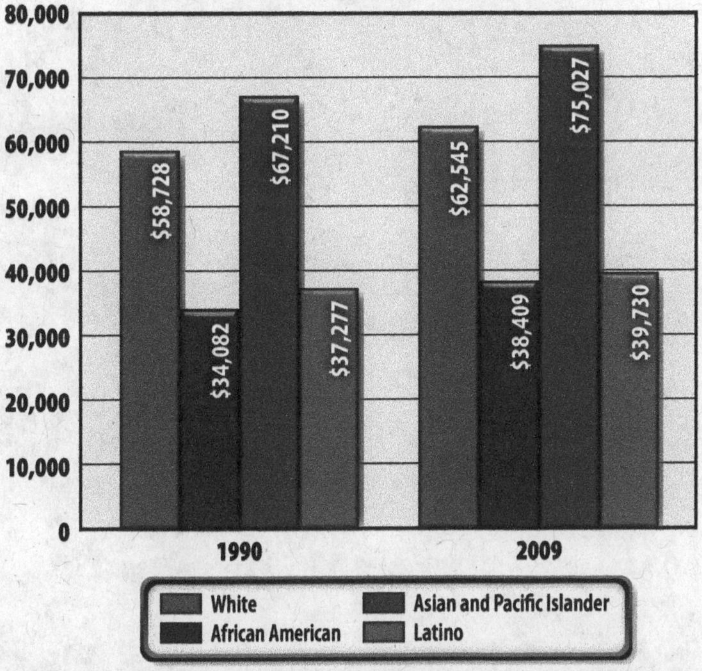

Source: U.S. Census Bureau, *Statistical Abstract of the United States: 2012,* Table 697

The graph tracks the correlation of income and race in the United States. What are three reasons income for non-white groups differs from income for white groups? How has income changed over the years shown in the graph?

22. In its landmark 1954 ruling in *Brown* v. *Board of Education of Topeka, Kansas,* the Supreme Court of the United States overturned policies that permitted segregation in public education.

However, institutionalized segregation nonetheless remains in place in public education in some places. What are some causes of this?

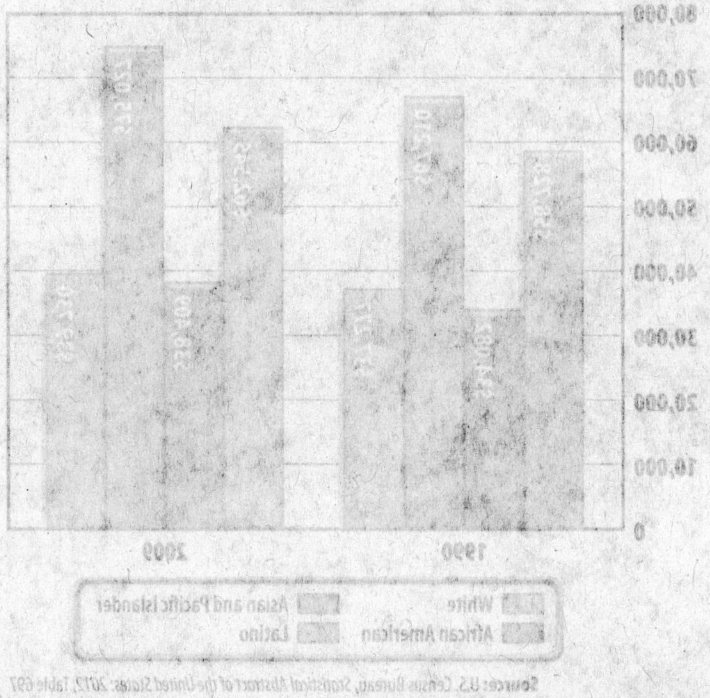

NAME ______________________ DATE ______________ CLASS __________

Lesson Quiz 10-1

networks

Inequalities of Gender and Age

DIRECTIONS: Modified True/False In the blank, indicate whether the statement is true (T) or false (F). If false, edit the statement to make it a true statement.

_______ **1.** In most cultures, girls are treated differently than boys virtually from the moment they are born.

_______ **2.** There are fewer variations within each sex than there are between the sexes.

_______ **3.** Men's brains tend to be more specialized than women's brains.

_______ **4.** Most sociologists believe that gender-related behavior is primarily the result of biology.

_______ **5.** Gender refers to an awareness of being masculine or feminine based on biology.

DIRECTIONS: Multiple Choice Indicate the answer choice that best completes the statement or answers the question.

_______ **6.** Which of the following best describes the relationship between sex and gender identity?

A. Boys behave differently than girls from the time they are born, so parents treat them differently.

B. Parents treat girls differently from boys, which makes the child aware of being male or female.

C. Because women can give birth to children, they are more valued by society, and therefore receive better treatment.

D. It has been scientifically proven that behavioral differences between boys and girls are linked to biological characteristics.

_______ **7.** The theory that behavioral differences are the result of inherited physical characteristics is called

A. biological determinism.
C. nature versus nurture.
B. gender identity.
D. adaptive evolution.

_______ **8.** Gender identity is awareness of being masculine or feminine based on

A. being male or female.
C. genetic differences.
B. social and cultural patterns.
D. biological facts.

_______ **9.** Men and women differ in what they look for in a potential mate. Most men value

A. a mate who is intelligent.
C. a mate who is physically attractive.
B. a mate who is older than they are.
D. a mate with a higher level of income.

_______ **10.** Most sociologists believe that definitions of masculinity and femininity are based on

A. research.
C. common knowledge.
B. tradition.
D. inherited truth.

NAME ______________________________ DATE ________________ CLASS ____________

Lesson Quiz 10-2

networks

Inequalities of Gender and Age

DIRECTIONS: Completion Write the word or phrase that correctly completes the statement.

1. Conflict theory believes that men have maintained their controlling role in government in order to ________________.

2. According to functionalism, in order to ensure the group survival, early humans created a division of labor ________________

3. A seven-year-old girl's mother encourages her to care for her infant cousin. However, her nine-year-old brother goes outside to play with friends. This is an example of ________________.

4. The sociologists that focus on the ways gender is acquired through communication with other people are ________________.

5. Both functionalism and conflict theory regard traditional gender roles as ________________.

DIRECTIONS: Multiple Choice Indicate the answer choice that best answers the question.

________ **6.** According to functionalism, any pattern of behavior that does not benefit society will become

- **A.** unimportant.
- **B.** enhanced.
- **C.** more important.
- **D.** more efficient.

________ **7.** Which of the following best describes the symbolic interactionist view of gender?

- **A.** It is to men's advantage to prevent women from gaining political, economic, and social power.
- **B.** Traditional gender roles are outdated because people no longer need to rely on physical strength to survive.
- **C.** The traditional division of responsibilities exists because it has benefited society.
- **D.** Children acquire their gender identity by interacting with people in the world around them.

________ **8.** Today, conflict theorists view gender roles as

- **A.** politically important.
- **B.** outdated.
- **C.** limiting the power of men.
- **D.** encouraging female dominance.

________ **9.** Which best describes how peers influence the gender socialization of high school students?

- **A.** They typically encourage each other to try nontraditional behavior.
- **B.** They typically encourage each other to follow traditional gender roles.
- **C.** Boys typically encourage other boys to follow nontraditional gender roles, while girls typically encourage other girls to follow traditional behavior.
- **D.** They have no influence on gender socialization.

________ **10.** When do symbolic interactionists believe that gender socialization begins?

- **A.** at birth
- **B.** in infancy
- **C.** in early childhood
- **D.** during adolescence

NAME ______________________________ DATE ____________________ CLASS __________

Lesson Quiz 10-3

networks

Inequalities of Gender and Age

DIRECTIONS: True/False In the blank, indicate whether the statement is true (T) or false (F).

______ **1.** A waitress in a diner is an example of a "pink-collar" job.

______ **2.** The United States has one of the lowest percentages of women holding elected office of any nation in the Western world.

______ **3.** In recent years, the number of women working outside the home has remained about the same.

______ **4.** Sexism is a set of attitudes, beliefs, and values used to justify gender inequality.

______ **5.** Since 1990, more men then women continue their education in graduate school.

DIRECTIONS: Multiple Choice Indicate the answer choice that best completes the statement or answers the question.

______ **6.** The majority of women

A. do not work outside the home.

B. with small children do not work outside the home.

C. earn 95 cents for every dollar men earn.

D. physicians and lawyers do not suffer from the earnings gap.

______ **7.** Margie wants to enroll in her school's advanced math class, but her counselor discourages her by saying the class is very difficult and she will be the only girl in the class. This is an example of

A. biological determinism. **C.** gender identity.

B. sexism. **D.** ageism.

______ **8.** Assume that 92% of all registered nurses are women. Which of the following best describes this situation?

A. *de jure* sexism **C.** biological determinism

B. occupational sex segregation **D.** sociological determinism

______ **9.** Which of the following is true about women's earnings?

A. Women earn about the same as men.

B. A significant percentage of women now earn more than men.

C. Women work about six days to earn as much as men earn in five days.

D. Most women earn less so that they can stay home more often.

______ **10.** How do recent college enrollment levels for women compare with those for men?

A. Fewer women are enrolling in college.

B. Most college students are men.

C. Enrollment levels are about the same for men and women.

D. Women now outnumber men in college.

NAME _______________ DATE _______________ CLASS _______________

Lesson Quiz 10-4

networks

Inequalities of Gender and Age

DIRECTIONS: True/False In the blank, indicate whether the statement is true (T) or false (F).

_______ **1.** One cause of ageism in a technological society is that the job skills of workers are more likely to be out of date than in an agricultural society.

_______ **2.** According to conflict theory, ageism is a way of forcing older people from the work force.

_______ **3.** Symbolic interactionists claim that ageism is primarily a biological condition.

_______ **4.** Age can be an advantage or a disadvantage for people in any age group.

_______ **5.** As the United States has become more industrialized, the elderly have achieved greater status.

DIRECTIONS: Multiple Choice Indicate the answer choice that best completes the statement or answers the question.

_______ **6.** Conflict theorists say that ageism

A. is learned in the same way that racism is learned.

B. is caused by competition for scarce resources.

C. occurs because in a technologically oriented society, a person is valued less when he or she is no longer working for a living.

D. occurs because American society has never valued the elderly.

_______ **7.** How do symbolic interactionists explain ageism?

A. Ageism is the result of competition over scarce resources.

B. Children learn negative attitudes about the elderly in the same way that they learn other prejudices.

C. Elderly people are not valued in technological society because their skills are outdated.

D. Ageism exists because society has more workers than there are jobs to fill.

_______ **8.** Consider the expression: "You can't teach an old dog new tricks." Which of the following best describes this statement?

A. It is an example of ageism.

B. It is an example of sexism.

C. It is an example of gender identity.

D. It is true.

_______ **9.** What phrase refers to the unequal distribution of scarce resources in a society based on age?

A. age discrimination

B. age stratification

C. gray power

D. ageism

_______ **10.** According to functionalists, attitudes about aging changed when

A. industrialization changed the nature of work.

B. new political systems emerged.

C. women began to enter the workforce.

D. the retirement age increased.

NAME ______________________ DATE ______________ CLASS ____________

Lesson Quiz 10-5

networks

Inequalities of Gender and Age

DIRECTIONS: Completion Write the word or phrase that correctly completes the statement.

1. Compared to other age groups, elderly Americans are more likely to exercise their right to ______________.

2. One reason that elderly Americans have not fully realized their potential political power is that they are a ______________,

3. One of the poorest segments of American society consists of ______________.

4. Compared with white Americans, poverty rates among African Americans are ______________.

5. Poverty levels among the elderly can be distorted because there are a smaller number of older people with ______________.

DIRECTIONS: Multiple Choice Indicate the answer choice that best answers the question.

________ **6.** Which of the following statements is true concerning the elderly in the United States today?

A. Few elderly women live in poverty because their husbands provide security.
B. The elderly are worse off than they were 40 years ago.
C. Most elderly people who live in institutions are financially well off.
D. Discrimination against racial minorities increases as people age.

________ **7.** Which of the following best describes the term *gray power*?

A. the belief among young people that older people serve no useful purpose in society
B. older people working out in gyms so that they will be physically stronger and live healthier lives
C. the increasing political power of the elderly
D. the increasing poverty of the elderly

________ **8.** Why do some politicians try to court the elderly in America?

A. The elderly tend to vote in greater numbers than other age groups.
B. The elderly have a higher level of spendable income than other groups
C. The elderly population is not diverse and are easy to sway.
D. The elderly make fewer demands on government social programs.

________ **9.** Which of the following is true regarding the economic status of the elderly over the past four decades?

A. They are much worse off today.
B. Poverty levels have remained steady.
C. The elderly are better off now.
D. Poverty no longer remains a problem.

________ **10.** Why do sociologists regard the elderly as a minority group?

A. because many older Americans are minorities
B. so that they can receive help from the government
C. because there are fewer older people
D. to expose stereotyping and discrimination

NAME ______________________________ DATE ______________ CLASS __________

Chapter 10 Test, Form A

networks

Inequalities of Gender and Age

DIRECTIONS: Matching Match each item with the correct statement below.

_______ **1.** Geraldine Ferraro	**A.** an employer uses beliefs to justify firing an older person
_______ **2.** Sandra Day O'Connor	**B.** a classification system that distinguishes boys from girls
_______ **3.** age stratification	**C.** an organization that influences political decision-making
_______ **4.** ageism	**D.** a society's image of how men and women should behave
_______ **5.** sex	**E.** a system in which a society offers more resources to young people than to the elderly
_______ **6.** occupational sex segregation	**F.** parents teach their children that some toys are for boys and others for girls
_______ **7.** interest group	**G.** the first woman appointed to the U.S. Supreme Court
_______ **8.** gender socialization	**H.** the first female candidate for vice president in U.S. history
_______ **9.** social security	**I.** when all of the nurses at a local hospital are women
_______ **10.** gender	**J.** a government program created to benefit older people

DIRECTIONS: Multiple Choice Indicate the answer choice that best completes the statement or answers the question.

_______ **11.** About 85% of corporate secretaries are female. This is an example of

A. gender identity.

B. biological determinism.

C. *de jure* sexism.

D. occupational sex segregation.

_______ **12.** What does the phrase biological determinism mean?

A. Females are genetically more aggressive then men.

B. Because they give birth to offspring, all females are good mothers.

C. Behavioral differences in males and females are a result of inherited characteristics.

D. It has been determined that biology is the key to gender identity.

_______ **13.** Most sociologists believe that

A. gender differences have both biological and cultural causes.

B. family attitudes are responsible for virtually all gender differences.

C. biology is responsible for about 90% of gender differences.

D. culture is responsible for about 90% of gender differences.

Chapter 10 Test, Form A *cont.*

networks

Inequalities of Gender and Age

______ **14.** Conflict theory claims that more powerful age groups use __________ to remove elderly competitors from the workforce.

A. the legal system
B. political power
C. forced retirement
D. physical force

______ **15.** Which of the following best describes the functionalist view of gender?

A. It is to men's advantage to prevent women from gaining political, economic, and social power.
B. Traditional gender roles are outdated because people in modern society no longer need to rely on physical strength to survive.
C. The traditional division of responsibilities between men and women exists because it has benefited society.
D. Children acquire their gender identity by interacting with the world around them, including parents, teachers, and peers.

______ **16.** In the 1800s, some schools had rules that female teachers had to be unmarried because most people believed that married women should stay home and take care of their families. However, no such rules applied to men in their work. This is an example of

A. biological determinism.
B. feminization of poverty.
C. sexism.
D. gender identity.

______ **17.** How does sex differ from gender?

A. Sex is shaped by culture.
B. Gender is a biological concept.
C. Cultural patterns are part of gender.
D. Behavior is determined by sex alone.

______ **18.** Which of the following is true regarding poverty among elderly Americans?

A. Elderly Americans are economically worse off than they were four decades ago.
B. The income gap between the wealthy elderly and the elderly poor is small.
C. Elderly women have a lower rate of poverty than elderly men.
D. The poverty rate for racial and ethnic minority elderly is higher than the poverty rate for whites.

______ **19.** Which of the following is true of how gender socialization occurs in schools?

A. Teachers encourage different behaviors from boys and girls.
B. Boys are taught to dislike math and science.
C. Girls are taught to dislike reading.
D. Boys are encouraged to be less assertive in class.

_______ **20.** Symbolic interactionists understand ageism as

A. a competition for resources.

B. a struggle for power.

C. the socialization of stereotypes.

D. the result of industrialization.

DIRECTIONS: Essays Answer the following questions on a separate sheet of paper.

21. Does biology or socialization appear to play a greater role in gender differences in America today? Explain your answer.

22.

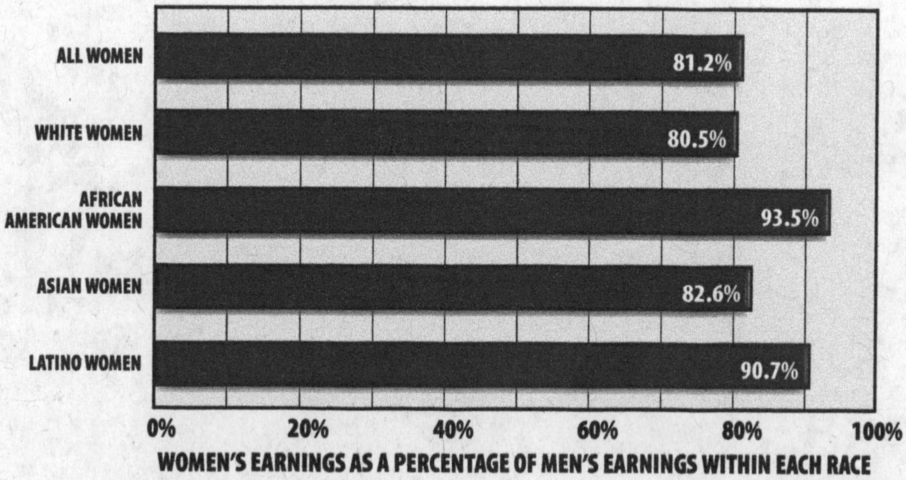

Source: "Highlights of Women's Earnings in 2010," U.S. Department of Labor, U.S. Bureau of Labor Statistics, July 2011, Table 1, p. 9

The graph illustrates women's earnings as a percentage of men's earnings by race. What are two factors that can explain the differences? Why do you think the differences in the wages paid to women and men exist? How do you think wage disparity should be addressed?

23. In studying gender behavior in primitive societies, cultural anthropologist Margaret Mead observed that over and over again the personalities of men and women have been seen as clearly contrasting, complementary, and opposite. Discuss how this observation helps explain the expectations people have about gender in the United States today?

Chapter 10 Test, Form A cont.

networks

Inequalities of Gender and Age

NAME _______________ DATE _______________ CLASS _______________

Chapter 10 Test, Form B

networks

Inequalities of Gender and Age

DIRECTIONS: Matching Match each item with the correct statement below.

_______ **1.** biological determinism

_______ **2.** "pink-collar" job

_______ **3.** Gray Panthers

_______ **4.** occupational sex segregation

_______ **5.** gender apartheid

_______ **6.** Margaret Mead

_______ **7.** Sonia Sotomayor

_______ **8.** Medicare

_______ **9.** age stratification

_______ **10.** sexism

A. a program designed to benefit elderly people

B. a cultural anthropologist who studied gender behavior

C. a group organized by elderly people to influence political decision making

D. employment that is considered to be mostly for women

E. an extreme form of discrimination against women that is practiced by some societies

F. a judge appointed to the United States Supreme Court by President Obama

G. when values and beliefs are used to justify discrimination against women

H. a belief that behavior is based on physical characteristics

I. age-based unequal distribution of societal resources

J. the concentration of one gender in lower-status occupations

DIRECTIONS: Multiple Choice Indicate the answer choice that best completes the statement or answers the question.

_______ **11.** Functionalists explain the loss of status among older people as a consequence of

A. discrimination.

B. class struggle.

C. industrialization.

D. socialization.

_______ **12.** In the United States, men tend to prefer mates who

A. are younger than they are.

B. are better off financially then they are.

C. are older than they are.

D. have a higher social status than they have.

_______ **13.** Which of the following illustrates the symbolic interactionist perspective on gender differences?

A. Women are denied access to education.

B. Men hunted, and women raised children.

C. Parents teach children gender roles.

D. Men earn more than women.

_______ **14.** Why is poverty among elderly Americans sometimes difficult to measure?

A. It is difficult to conduct surveys among the elderly.

B. There is an income gap that distorts the overall picture.

C. Most elderly Americans no longer work.

D. All elderly Americans benefit from government programs.

_______ **15.** Women held less than ten percent of civil engineering positions in 2010. This is an example of

A. occupational sex segregation.

B. *de jure* segregation.

C. gender socialization.

D. a "pink-collar" job.

_______ **16.** Which of the following statements best expresses the belief of most sociologists regarding gender differences?

A. Biology is responsible for about 90% of gender differences.

B. Culture is responsible for about 90% of gender differences.

C. Family attitudes are responsible for about 75% of gender differences.

D. Both biology and culture are responsible for gender differences.

_______ **17.** Which of the following is an example of a "pink-collar" job?

A. secretary

B. manager of a small business

C. economist

D. taxi driver

_______ **18.** A successful businesswoman suddenly finds that she cannot be promoted to the top levels of her company. Conflict theorists call this a

A. glass ceiling.

B. social ladder.

C. brick wall.

D. social pattern.

_______ **19.** Which of the following is true about the median age of people in the United States?

A. It has remained about the same.

B. More people are older now.

C. The median age is younger.

D. The population is declining.

______ **20.** Which of the following is true regarding voter turnout and age?

A. People are more likely to vote as they get older.

B. Young people vote in greater numbers than older people.

C. Elderly people have less difficulty getting to the polls.

D. Voting rates are about the same for all age groups.

DIRECTIONS: Essay Answer the following questions on a separate sheet of paper.

21. Gerontologists report that a significant portion of the American population (about 12%) is over the age of 65. Describe the concept of ageism and list positive and negative ways the elderly are described.

"Such a system would be wasteful of the gifts of many women who could exercise other functions far better than the ability to bear children in an already overpopulated world. It would be wasteful of the gifts of many men who could exercise their special personality gifts far better in the home than in the market-place. It would be wasteful, but it would be clear. It could attempt to guarantee to each individual the role for which society insisted upon training him or her, and such a system would penalize only those individuals who, in spite of all the training, did not display the approved personalities."

— Margaret Mead, from *Sex and Temperament in Three Primitive Societies*.

Credit: *Excerpt from pp. 290 – 1 {"There are at least three courses… approved personalities."} from Sex and Temperament in Three Primitive Societies* by Margaret Mead. Copyright © 1935, 1950, 1963 by Margaret Mead. Reprinted by permission of HarperCollins Publishers.

22. This quote questions gender roles in her 1935 study of three primitive, or preliterate, societies. It was published in 1935. Mead suggests that women have roles in society that are assigned to them based on their sex. Do you think her observations hold true today in modern industrial societies? What important scientific changes may have altered Mead's findings in the intervening years?

NAME ______________________________ DATE ________________ CLASS ____________

Lesson Quiz 11-1

networks

The Family

DIRECTIONS: Matching Match each item with the correct statement below.

_______ **1.** patriarchy

_______ **2.** nuclear family

_______ **3.** monogamy

_______ **4.** extended family

_______ **5.** polygamy

A. most families take this form in postindustrial societies

B. a structure in which one man is married to one woman

C. close adult relatives living together

D. a structure that is also referred to as *plural marriage*

E. a family structure in which the father has authority

DIRECTIONS: Multiple Choice Indicate the answer choice that best completes the statement or answers the question.

_______ **6.** Juan lives with his parents and three siblings. Next month his grandmother will be moving in with his family, creating a(n) ______________ family.

A. exogenous

B. patriarchal

C. nuclear

D. extended

_______ **7.** Which of the following is a common characteristic of the American family today?

A. Inheritance is patrilineal.

B. It is usually matrilocal.

C. The marriage is monogamous.

D. It is a patriarchy.

_______ **8.** Which of the following is true of the definition of a family?

A. A family is a complex social unit.

B. The family has less impact on individuals than other social institutions.

C. A family is a group related by blood only.

D. People can only be born into a family.

_______ **9.** What is the pattern of residence practiced by most American couples?

A. neolocal

B. patrilocal

C. matrilocal

D. polygyny

_______ **10.** Which of the following is the only legally acceptable form of marriage in the United States?

A. polygamy

B. monogamy

C. polygyny

D. polyandry

NAME ____________________ DATE ____________ CLASS ____________

Lesson Quiz 11-2

networks

The Family

DIRECTIONS: True/False In the blank, indicate whether the statement is true (T) or false (F).

_______ **1.** Symbolic interactionists focus on the ways that family members interact with one another.

_______ **2.** Many conflict theorists believe that the family is the source of equality between men and women.

_______ **3.** One important function of the family is to provide emotional support and acceptance.

_______ **4.** For functionalists, the family is a structure whose main role is to encourage competition among family members.

_______ **5.** According to symbolic interactionists, relations among family members remain stable and unchanging.

DIRECTIONS: Multiple Choice Indicate the answer choice that best completes the statement or answers the question.

_______ **6.** Which of the following theoretical perspectives emphasizes that families have many roles, including transmitting social status, regulating sexual activity, and providing economic and social support?

A. symbolic interactionism
B. cultural pluralism
C. functionalism
D. conflict theory

_______ **7.** Which of the following best describes the symbolic interactionist view of the family?

A. The primary purpose of the family is to regulate sexual activity.
B. An important role of the family is the socialization of children and the development of their self-concept.
C. Traditionally, the male has controlled the family and the female has been seen as his helper.
D. Married couples should live with the husband or wife's parents in order to care for them in their old age.

_______ **8.** An important function of the family is to accept and love all of its members. This function is referred to as

A. cohabitation.
B. socio-emotional maintenance.
C. the reproductive function of the family.
D. transmitting social status.

_______ **9.** Which of the following best describes the economic function of the family?

A. A family provides socio-emotional maintenance for its members.
B. Families teach young people to abstain from sex before marriage.
C. Adult family members work outside the home to earn income to meet the family's needs.
D. The family unit is the primary way to support, raise, and socialize offspring.

_______ **10.** According to conflict theorists, the family has a built-in

A. gender inequality.
B. socio-emotional function.
C. economic function.
D. system of socialization.

NAME ______________________ DATE ______________ CLASS ____________

Lesson Quiz 11-3

networks

The Family

DIRECTIONS: Completion Indicate the answer choice that best completes the statement.

1. Most Americans say that the best reason to get married is for ______________.

2. People are less likely to get divorced when they have been married a ______________.

3. Psychologists report that in families, physical violence can be as damaging as ______________.

4. Since 1940, the marriage rate in the United States has ______________.

5. One form of family violence is ______________.

DIRECTIONS: Multiple Choice Indicate the answer choice that best answers the question.

_______ **6.** American families are typically

A. extended.

B. neolocal.

C. polygyny.

D. nonegalitarian.

_______ **7.** What is one reason that sociologists believe the divorce rate in the United States will continue to decline?

A. Economic conditions have improved.

B. The average age of the population is increasing.

C. People are getting married earlier in life.

D. Couples are having more children.

_______ **8.** About how many incidents of child abuse are reported in the United States each year?

A. three thousand

B. thirty thousand

C. three hundred thousand

D. three million, three hundred thousand

_______ **9.** What phrase best describe the term sibling violence?

A. hostility among children in a family

B. parent-child physical abuse

C. abuse of one adult partner by the other

D. bullying by classmates

_______ **10.** Which of the following is true about domestic violence?

A. It occurs at all social class levels.

B. Children are rarely victims.

C. Verbal abuse is not considered a form of domestic violence.

D. Domestic violence rarely affects the elderly.

NAME ______________________ DATE ______________ CLASS ________

Lesson Quiz 11-4

networks

The Family

DIRECTIONS: True/False In the blank, indicate whether the statement is true (T) or false (F).

_______ **1.** In some states, individuals can marry a person of the same sex or the opposite sex.

_______ **2.** Research shows that cohabitations do not last as long as marriages.

_______ **3.** One reason for the increase in blended families is the relatively low rate of divorce.

_______ **4.** Many sociologists believe that the nuclear family is disappearing from American life.

_______ **5.** In the future, more couples will face the prospect of caring for children and elderly parents.

DIRECTIONS: Multiple Choice Indicate the answer choice that best completes the statement or answers the question.

_______ **6.** Which of the following is most likely to be true in a two-income family?

A. Tasks such as housework are shared equally by the husband and wife.

B. Wives are still expected to perform most of the housework and child care, even though they have full-time jobs.

C. Most of the child care is performed by the husband, while wives do most of the housework.

D. The psychological well-being of the wife is diminished because she is not a full-time mother.

_______ **7.** Which of the following best describes the future of the nuclear family in the United States?

A. The nuclear family will remain the most common institution for raising children.

B. As women become increasingly economically independent, the nuclear family will decline.

C. Couples will marry less and will typically live in separate households.

D. Economic pressures will cause more children to be raised by extended family members.

_______ **8.** Which of the following is a positive effect of dual employment?

A. It simplifies the job of child rearing.

B. It improves the family's structure.

C. It tends to improve the psychological well-being of women.

D. It burdens the husband with the task of child rearing.

_______ **9.** Which of the following statements concerning marriage is true?

A. More people are choosing to remain unmarried than ever before in American history.

B. Fewer people are cohabitating today because it has become socially unacceptable.

C. All states now recognize same-sex marriages.

D. Most American families are patriarchal.

_______ **10.** Which of the following is true of single-parent families?

A. They are likely to be blended families.

B. About 80 percent of them are headed by women.

C. They have higher rates of household income.

D. Most single parents choose to remain unmarried.

NAME ______________________________ DATE ______________ CLASS __________

Chapter 11 Test, Form A

networks

The Family

DIRECTIONS: Matching Match each item with the correct statement below.

_______ **1.** egalitarian

_______ **2.** socio-emotional maintenance

_______ **3.** polygamy

_______ **4.** endogamy

_______ **5.** marriage rate

_______ **6.** blended family

_______ **7.** patriarchy

_______ **8.** adolescent

_______ **9.** two-income marriage

_______ **10.** polyandry

A. both a child's mother and father work outside the home

B. a man with children marries a woman with children from a previous marriage

C. this number has fallen by about 50 percent since World War II

D. a relationship in which authority is split evenly between a husband and a wife

E. being allowed to marry only a person within one's religious background

F. marriage to more than one person at the same time

G. a relationship in which the man makes the important decisions in his family

H. a family provides acceptance and support for its members

I. a person between the ages of 12 and 17

J. a rare form of marriage in which a woman has more than one husband at the same time

DIRECTIONS: Multiple Choice Indicate the answer choice that best completes the statement or answers the question.

_______ **11.** Which of the following is a pattern in the American family?

A. Inheritance is traced only through the husband's family.
B. Inheritance is traced only through the wife's family.
C. Both partners share in decision making.
D. Households today typically contain multiple sets of parents and children.

_______ **12.** Many societies do not allow first cousins to marry because

A. it is a violation of norms against polygamy.
B. it is a violation of the incest taboo.
C. it will be difficult for them to achieve economic success.
D. it is a violation of norms against endogamy.

_______ **13.** In a ____________________ society, descent is traced through the female side of the family.

A. monogamous
B. bilateral
C. matrilineal
D. matrilocal

_______ **14.** Which of the following best describes the reproductive function of the family?

A. Family provides an orderly and regulated system for producing new members

B. Families teach young people to abstain from sex before marriage.

C. Adult family members work outside the home to generate income that is spent to meet the family's needs.

D. A society cannot survive without new members, and the family unit is the best way to raise and socialize them.

_______ **15.** What do sociologists believe will happen to the divorce rate in the coming years?

A. It will go up sharply.

B. It will remain about the same.

C. It will continue to decline dramatically.

D. It will decline somewhat.

_______ **16.** Which of the following behaviors is a common trait of families?

A. authority

B. polygamy

C. polyandry

D. political ideology

_______ **17.** Many sociologists believe that in the future

A. the nuclear family will continue to decline in number.

B. divorce rates will rise sharply.

C. the trend toward more working parents will continue.

D. extended families will become more popular.

_______ **18.** Which of the following is true about most families in the United States?

A. Families are nuclear.

B. Families are polygamous.

C. Wedding ceremonies are the same across all cultures.

D. Families are patrilocal.

_______ **19.** Which of the following is true of same-sex marriages in the United States?

A. The stigma surrounding homosexuality has disappeared completely.

B. Several states have legalized same-sex marriage.

C. All Federal courts have banned same-sex marriage.

D. Gay couples in all states can form "civil unions."

Chapter 11 Test, Form A *cont.*

The Family

_______ **20.** Which of the following contributes to the declining divorce rate seen in the United States?

A. The average age of first marriage is rising.

B. Women are punished socially for leaving a marriage.

C. The rising number of children in families.

D. A lack of respect between the partners.

DIRECTIONS: Essays Answer the following questions on a separate sheet of paper.

21.

"... The school selectively validated certain cultural practices as legitimate. Other practices such as hitting children, while virtually universal in other historical periods were deemed unacceptable. Adherence to the practice of the accomplishment of natural growth, rather than concerted cultivation, had important consequences when the families interacted with the school. The Yanelli family keenly felt the school to be a threatening force, In other words their failure to use elaborate reasoning (a cultural practice) was transformed into a lack of resources when they confronted school resources. They felt worried powerless and scared."

—*Unequal Childhoods: Class, Race, and Family Life*, by Annette Lareau, © 2010 by the Regents of the University of California. Published by the University of California Press.

In what ways might family relationships help establish effective and productive relationships with schools?

22. List three components that characterize the basic nature of the American family, and explain the significance of each.

23. What is the legal status of the various possible marriage arrangements in America today?

NAME ______________________________ DATE ____________________ CLASS ____________

Chapter 11 Test, Form B

networks

The Family

DIRECTIONS: Matching Match each item with the correct statement below.

______ **1.** patrilocal

______ **2.** incest taboo

______ **3.** divorce rate

______ **4.** feminists

______ **5.** neolocal

______ **6.** cohabitation

______ **7.** extended family

______ **8.** boomerang kid

______ **9.** matriarchy

______ **10.** polygyny

A. parents and children living with their grandparents and sharing resources

B. arrangement in which a married couple lives together on their own

C. arrangement in which a romantic couple lives together while not legally married

D. a young adult who moves back in with his parents

E. a law against marrying a first cousin

F. a marriage in which a man has more than one wife at the same time

G. a family in which the oldest woman in the family holds all of the authority

H. this increased dramatically in America from 1960–1981

I. arrangement in which a married couple lives with the husband's parents

J. writers and activists who organize on behalf of women's rights and interests

DIRECTIONS: Multiple Choice Indicate the answer choice that best completes the statement or answers the question.

______ **11.** How does conflict theory explain the roles and functions of families?

A. Families function better when a female works outside of the home.

B. In the past, families fostered social equality.

C. In a family setting, women have the ability to provide for themselves.

D. Historically male dominance has been considered "legitimate."

______ **12.** What is one reason for the phenomenon of boomerang kids?

A. Young adults are getting married earlier.

B. Many young adults cannot afford to live on their own.

C. Most young adults return home to help support their families.

D. Single parent households encourage young adults to live at home.

______ **13.** Which of the following institutions has the greatest effect on individual behavior?

A. the government

B. schools

C. peer groups

D. the family

_______ **14.** Domestic violence in the United States

A. occurs in all social classes.

B. is limited to spousal abuse.

C. occurs mostly in the lower classes.

D. does not occur in very religious homes.

_______ **15.** Which of the following norms is a person of the Islamic faith most likely to have violated by marrying a Christian?

A. exogamy

B. polygamy

C. endogamy

D. monogamy

_______ **16.** Tara lives with her father, stepmother, and her stepmother's children from a previous marriage. What type of family does she live in?

A. patriarchal

B. extended

C. blended

D. single parent

_______ **17.** When Ben's family needs to make a major decision, such as purchasing a new home or car, his father makes the decision without consulting other family members. This is an example of

A. a patriarchy.

B. polygamy.

C. a patrilineal family.

D. a neolocal family.

_______ **18.** Which of the following is a probable reason for the recent decline in the divorce rate?

A. Families are having more children.

B. Couples are marrying for the first time at a younger age.

C. More women are working outside the home, even when they have preschool children.

D. Children are spaced further apart.

_______ **19.** In the United States, the only legally acceptable form of marriage is

A. polygyny.

B. monogamy.

C. polyandry.

D. polygamy.

_______ **20.** For conflict theorists, ______________ is one consequence of the family structure.

A. socio-emotional support

B. the socialization of children

C. inequality among men and women

D. the production of needed goods

DIRECTIONS: Essay Answer the following questions on a separate sheet of paper.

21.

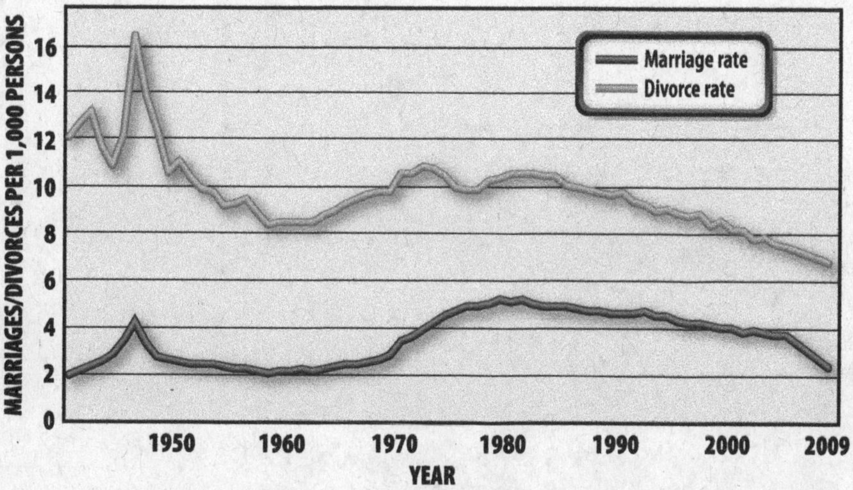

Source: U.S. Census Bureau, Statistical Abstract of the United States: 2012.

The graph shows the rate of marriages and divorces in the United States since 1940. In what year was the marriage rate the highest? In what year was the divorce rate the highest? What is the overall trend for both divorce and marriage in the United States?

What are two reasons to account for the data shown in the graph?

22. The chapter shows that families and marriages take many different forms in different societies. What are some rituals you know about in wedding ceremonies? What do these rituals suggest about the values of the culture that performs them?

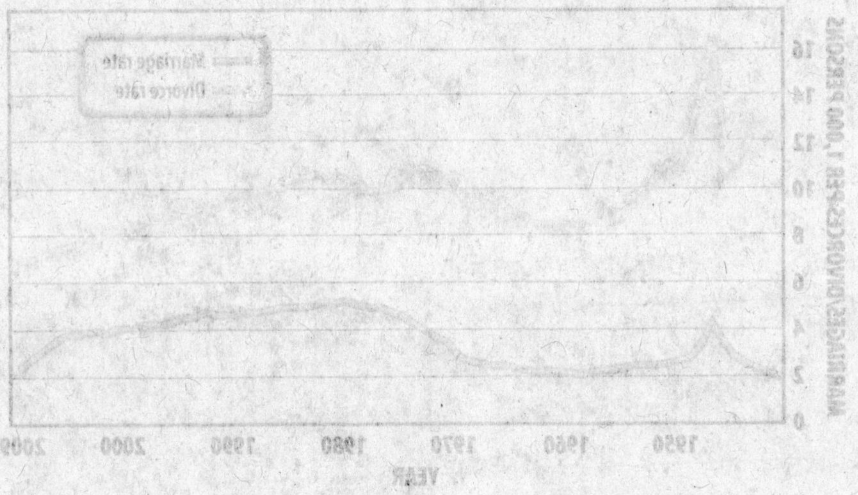

NAME ______________________ DATE ______________ CLASS __________

Lesson Quiz 12-1

networks

Education

DIRECTIONS: True/False In the blank, indicate whether the statement is true (T) or false (F).

_______ **1.** A traditional classroom is less authoritarian than an open-classroom setting.

_______ **2.** The bureaucratic model of education responds to the creative, expressive, and emotional needs of all children.

_______ **3.** Critics of for-profit schools argue that they will be less responsive to public input than traditional public schools.

_______ **4.** Charter schools are public schools, but they have more freedom in establishing their curriculum than traditional schools.

_______ **5.** One goal of the back-to-basics movement was to abandon the bureaucratic model of education.

DIRECTIONS: Multiple Choice Indicate the answer choice that best completes the statement or answers the question.

_______ **6.** Which of the following is a characteristic of charter schools?

A. They are not public schools.

B. They are extremely bureaucratic.

C. They do not have to answer to a school board.

D. They cannot shape their own curriculum.

_______ **7.** Which of the following statements would most likely be made by a supporter of for-profit schools?

A. Schools can benefit from applying modern business practices to education.

B. Students can benefit by helping in developing the curricula they will be using.

C. Privately-run schools are more bureaucratic than publicly run schools.

D. All schools should be integrated, regardless of whether they are in the suburbs or inner-city.

_______ **8.** Which of the following best describes the voucher system?

A. Families are given government money to send their children to the school of their choice.

B. Students are placed into specific classes based on their scores on intelligence tests.

C. Public schools specialize in particular areas such as mathematics or the arts.

D. Voucher schools teach about the differences among gender, ethnic, and racial categories.

_______ **9.** Jim's class is learning about architecture by splitting up into groups to design and create scale models of buildings. This is an example of ______________ learning.

A. cooperative

B. magnet

C. back-to-basics

D. multicultural

_______ **10.** Traditional schools are bureaucratic primarily because

A. this method provides for multiple intelligences.

B. this method encourages democracy, which is important to American society.

C. it encourages the child to cooperate with other students and share ideas openly.

D. it is an efficient way of educating large numbers of children.

NAME ______________________________ DATE __________________ CLASS ____________

Lesson Quiz 12-2

networks

Education

DIRECTIONS: Completion Indicate the answer choice that best completes the statement.

1. For working parents, one important latent function of education is to ______________.

2. The goal of tracking is to place students in classes that align with their ______________.

3. An example of a manifest function of education is to promote a student's personal ______________.

4. Functionalists believe that schools provide the important function of transmitting ______________.

5. Some people support bilingual education because it encourages non-native speakers to ______________.

DIRECTIONS: Multiple Choice Indicate the answer choice that best answers the question.

________ 6. Which of the following is a latent function of a typical elementary school?

A. to teach children how to read

B. to teach children arithmetic

C. to provide day care for working parents.

D. to teach children how to reason

________ 7. Which of the following is a criticism of student tracking?

A. It hinders the development of a common American identity.

B. It unfairly labels students.

C. It relies too heavily on standardized curriculum.

D. It favors students in low-income areas.

________ 8. How do latent functions differ from manifest functions?

A. Latent functions are unintentional.

B. Only latent functions are a consequence of education.

C. Latent functions are always negative.

D. Latent functions produce a recognized result.

________ 9. Which of the following might be considered a latent function of a college education?

A. learning math and science

B. understanding American culture

C. creating a common identity

D. meeting a potential spouse

________ 10. Which of the following is a manifest function of education?

A. transmitting culture

B. creating a discordant identity

C. providing a training ground for athletes

D. teaching religious values

NAME ____________ DATE ____________ CLASS ____________

Lesson Quiz 12-3

networks

Education

DIRECTIONS: Matching Match each item with the correct statement below.

_______ **1.** educational equality

_______ **2.** multicultural education

_______ **3.** meritocracy

_______ **4.** compensatory education

_______ **5.** school desegregation

A. minorities and whites scoring about the same in school

B. the process of achieving racial balance in schools

C. a program designed to help disadvantaged children

D. a system based on competition

E. curriculum that also emphasizes the contributions of minorities

DIRECTIONS: Multiple Choice Indicate the answer choice that best completes the statement or answers the question.

_______ **6.** In order to have a positive effect on the academic achievement of minority children, school integration

A. can be instituted only in nontraditional schools.

B. must be done in an atmosphere of respect and acceptance.

C. must be instituted so that all of the children in the school live in the same neighborhood.

D. should be instituted only in inner-city schools.

_______ **7.** Which is an example of a compensatory educational program?

A. an open classroom

B. a charter school

C. a for-profit school

D. Head Start

_______ **8.** Which of the following is an advantage of a meritocracy?

A. People are encouraged to work hard because they believe it will lead to social and economic success.

B. Parents will be more likely to send their children to private schools because they will have the money to do so.

C. Students and teachers develop curricula together, providing a sense of democracy.

D. Reading, writing, and arithmetic are emphasized.

_______ **9.** Most social scientists consider intelligence to be

A. solely the result of genetic differences in people.

B. the result of the environment on different races.

C. a theory used to justify inequality.

D. a combination of inheritance and environmental effects.

_______ **10.** What is compensatory education?

A. race-based education programs

B. programs parents pay schools to adopt

C. programs to overcome educational deficits

D. classes with mandatory attendance requirements

NAME ______________________ DATE ______________ CLASS __________

Lesson Quiz 12-4

networks

Education

DIRECTIONS: True/False In the blank, indicate whether the statement is true (T) or false (F).

_______ **1.** If a textbook emphasizes the importance of men in American history but says very little about women, either negative or positive, it can still foster sexism.

_______ **2.** Many teachers intentionally transmit sexist attitudes to their students.

_______ **3.** Studies have shown that some students perform better than others simply because they are expected to do so.

_______ **4.** History textbooks have tended to give unbiased accounts of the past in order to teach civic responsibility.

_______ **5.** Boys attend college in greater numbers than girls.

DIRECTIONS: Multiple Choice Indicate the answer choice that best completes the statement or answers the question.

_______ **6.** Which of the following is an example of the hidden curriculum?

A. developing language and reading skills

B. having fourth-graders memorize their multiplication tables

C. encouraging children to be cooperative

D. teaching geography

_______ **7.** Studies show that girls are less likely to call out in class because

A. biology predisposes them to be quiet.

B. teachers socialize them to be quieter than boys.

C. girls are naturally more passive than boys.

D. they are uninterested in the subject matter.

_______ **8.** Why are girls in single-gender schools more likely to outperform girls in coeducational schools?

A. They use unbiased textbooks.

B. Expectations are lower.

C. Teachers give them more attention.

D. Math and science are not emphasized.

_______ **9.** One way that history textbooks develop patriotism is by

A. presenting different perspectives on historical events.

B. avoiding negative accounts of the country where the school is located.

C. offering critical accounts of a country's history.

D. revising the textbook to reflect recent changes.

_______ **10.** Which of the following is true about the hidden curriculum?

A. It sets out to teach a specific subject matter.

B. It is taught to girls, but not boys.

C. It often involves the teaching of social values such as cooperation.

D. It teaches content few people know about.

NAME ______________________ DATE ______________ CLASS __________

Chapter 12 Test, Form A

networks

Education

DIRECTIONS: Matching Match each item with the correct statement below.

_______ **1.** integrative curriculum

_______ **2.** tracking

_______ **3.** open-classroom

_______ **4.** meritocracy

_______ **5.** cultural bias

_______ **6.** charter school

_______ **7.** hidden curriculum

_______ **8.** educational equality

_______ **9.** school desegregation

_______ **10.** magnet school

A. something that is unfairly slanted in favor of certain groups

B. a system in which students do not compete for grades and there are no graded report cards

C. when lower class and minority students achieve the same results as all other students

D. students learn discipline by arriving to class on time

E. a school that receives public funding but shapes its own curriculum

F. the process of achieving racial balance in classrooms

G. a school which focuses on a specific subject or field of study

H. grouping students in classes as a result of test scores

I. a system in which social status depends on ability and achievement

J. students and teachers work together to decide the subject matter to be studied.

DIRECTIONS: Multiple Choice Indicate the answer choice that best completes the statement or answers the question.

_______ **11.** What is one way that manifest functions differ from latent functions?

A. Manifest functions are unintentional.

B. Only manifest functions have positive outcomes.

C. The consequences of manifest functions are recognized.

D. Manifest functions relate to education.

_______ **12.** Which of the following is true of the Scholastic Aptitude Test (SAT)?

A. African Americans obtain about the same scores on the SAT as whites.

B. Studies have shown that this test is a good measure of cognitive abilities.

C. Because minorities tend to go to lower-quality schools than whites, they are not as well prepared for the SAT.

D. Social class is not a major factor in SAT scores.

_______ **13.** Matt's science class is learning about botany by dividing into groups and performing experiments concerning plant growth. This is an example of

A. a charter school.

B. the voucher system.

C. cooperative learning.

D. the hidden curriculum.

_______ **14.** Rachel attends a school where she learns about a variety of social and ethnic traditions. Lessons include information about the holidays and home lives of peoples from a variety of backgrounds. Which of the following terms describes this approach to education?

A. multiculturalism

B. back-to-basics

C. self-fulfilling prophecy

D. integrative curriculum

_______ **15.** When students learn the value of cooperation by waiting in line during recess, this is an example of

A. the open-classroom.

B. the hidden curriculum.

C. cooperative learning.

D. formal schooling.

_______ **16.** Which of the following allows parents to receive educational money from the government and use it to pay tuition at a school of their choice?

A. traditional classrooms

B. back-to-basic methods

C. voucher systems

D. charter schools

_______ **17.** Which of the following statements best explains the primary purpose of compensatory educational programs?

A. to encourage students to be cooperative and work well with others

B. to improve the academic performance of children who are socially disadvantaged

C. to provide exposure to music and art at an early age

D. to provide free child care for parents

_______ **18.** Which of the following is associated with democratic reforms in the classroom?

A. distance learning programs

B. the factory method of education

C. the closed classroom

D. integrative curriculum

_______ **19.** Why do history textbooks tend to avoid negative information about the country where the textbooks are used?

A. to teach patriotism and civic duty

B. because space in the book is limited

C. teachers have asked them to

D. they want to sell more books

_______ **20.** Which of the following is a manifest function of education?

A. providing day care for working parents

B. lowering delinquency rates in adolescents

C. transmitting culture

D. creating jobs for people in education

DIRECTIONS: Essay Answer the following questions on a separate sheet of paper.

21. In addition to public school, there are other types of schools—including charter, magnet, private, and for-profit schools. If you had an opportunity to attend any of these schools when you were in elementary school, which one would you have chosen? Why?

22. Give examples of how the hidden curriculum operates in your school. In what ways might the hidden curriculum be negative or positive? Explain your response.

23.

> "The establishment of a republican government, without well-appointed and efficient means for the universal education of the people, is the most rash and fool-hardy experiment ever tried by man. . . . If such a republic be devoid of intelligence, it will only more closely resemble an obscene giant . . . whose brain has been developed only in the region of the appetites and passions, and not in the organs of reason and conscience."
>
> —from *Annual Reports of the Secretary of the Board of Education of Massachusetts 1845–1848*

The quote above was written by Horace Mann, an early advocate of universal public education in the United States. Why do you think Mann regards education as so important to democratic society? Do you agree with his claim? Why or why not?

NAME ______________________ DATE ______________ CLASS ______________

Chapter 12 Test, Form B

networks

Education

DIRECTIONS: Matching Match each item with the correct statement below.

_______ **1.** manifest function

_______ **2.** for-profit schools

_______ **3.** compensatory education

_______ **4.** multicultural education

_______ **5.** voucher system

_______ **6.** latent function

_______ **7.** formal schooling

_______ **8.** competition

_______ **9.** cooperative learning

_______ **10.** cognitive ability

A. the ability to reason and think abstractly

B. sports and meritocracies are based on this process

C. in this system, schools are supported and regulated by society

D. curriculum which emphasizes the contributions of minorities

E. schools run by private companies

F. an intended result of education, such as the teaching of academic skills

G. a system in which funds from the government can be used to help pay for private school

H. an unintentional result of education, such as using schools to lower delinquency by giving children a place to go

I. students working together to learn about something

J. One of the best-known examples of this is Head Start.

DIRECTIONS: Multiple Choice Indicate the answer choice that best completes the statement or answers the question.

_______ **11.** Why do functionalists distinguish between manifest and latent functions?

A. Consequences can be both negative and positive.

B. Institutions often have unintentional consequences.

C. Schools often leave some people out.

D. Education is not the only social institution.

_______ **12.** The "back-to-basics" movement came about because

A. many adults thought that students did not have enough freedom in the classroom.

B. many adults become concerned that students were not learning important subjects like reading and writing.

C. many adults thought that schools were not placing enough emphasis on the arts and athletics.

D. schools were becoming too bureaucratic.

_______ **13.** The rewards that an individual receives in a meritocracy are based primarily on

A. the status of the person's parents.

B. the person's intellectual abilities.

C. the person's race or ethnicity.

D. competition.

______ **14.** The term *Pygmalion effect* is sometimes used to describe one way teachers affect student performance. Which of the following is an example of this effect?

A. a teacher viewing a member of a minority as inferior

B. a student does better because she comes from a middle-class family

C. a student does better because the teacher expects the student to do better

D. a student does better because the teacher notices that the student is better behaved in class

______ **15.** Testing and grades do more than monitor students' comprehension of an academic subject. They also teach students the value of competition. This is an example of

A. meritocracy.

B. cognitive ability.

C. the hidden curriculum.

D. educational equality.

______ **16.** Some people believe for-profit schools are a good idea because

A. only the "best" schools will survive in the marketplace.

B. schools will be more integrated.

C. all schools will have the same curricula and standards.

D. these schools will have to answer to a local school board, which will set high standards.

______ **17.** In some schools, lower income and minority students achieve results that are comparable to those of all other students. This is an example of

A. school desegregation.

B. educational equality.

C. cognitive ability.

D. multiculturalism.

______ **18.** Why do some people oppose bilingual education in schools?

A. They worry that English will no longer be spoken in the United States.

B. They feel that it hinders the development of a common American identity.

C. They are concerned that non-native speakers will fall behind in their grade.

D. They want English to remain free from other linguistic influences.

______ **19.** What is one way commonly used to promote educational equality?

A. the hidden curriculum

B. desegregation

C. intelligence testing

D. competition among students

_______ **20.** One criticism of formal schooling is that it

A. is inefficient.

B. fails to produce a standardized curriculum.

C. lacks the flexibility to treat children as individuals.

D. is incapable of educating large numbers of children.

DIRECTIONS: Essay Answer the following questions on a separate sheet of paper.

21. Discuss the functionalist perspective that educational institutions, especially high schools, need to develop to meet society's needs.

22.

Educational Attainment by Sex: Selected Years, 1970–2010

High School Graduate or More	Male	Female	College Graduate or More	Male	Female
1970	51.9%	52.8%	1970	13.5%	8.1%
1980	67.3	65.8	1980	20.1	12.8
1990	77.7	77.5	1990	24.4	18.4
1995	81.7	81.6	1995	26.0	20.2
2000	84.2	84.0	2000	27.8	23.6
2005	84.9	85.5	2005	28.9	26.5
2010	86.6	87.6	2009	30.3	29.6

Source: U.S. Census Bureau, *Statistical Abstract of the United States: 2012*

This table shows educational attainment by gender. Compare the levels in 1970 with the levels in 2010. What can you conclude about rates for males and females in the high school graduation rates shown? What do the words "or more" mean in both high school and college rates? What is the most dramatic change you can observe in the chart's data for college graduates? What is one possible explanation for this change?

NAME ______________________ DATE ______________ CLASS ________

Lesson Quiz 13-1

networks

Political and Economic Institutions

DIRECTIONS: True/False In the blank, indicate whether the statement is true (T) or false (F).

______ **1.** The economic institution and the political institution should be thought of as two distinct and unrelated institutions.

______ **2.** Most modern governments are based on traditional authority.

______ **3.** Political scientists refer to the United States as a constitutional republic.

______ **4.** Representative democracy operates under the assumption that all people in modern society can be actively involved in all political decision-making.

______ **5.** Formal governmental structures arose with the development of agricultural economies and the rise of city-states.

DIRECTIONS: Multiple Choice Indicate the answer choice that best completes the statement or answers the question.

______ **6.** Which type of power does Nelson Mandela's rule exemplify?

A. coercive, because his power arose through a show of force

B. rational-legal, because his power arose from the office he held

C. traditional, because his power arose from legitimacy rooted in custom

D. charismatic, because his power arose from his personal characteristics

______ **7.** Suppose that a nation was formerly controlled by elected rulers who usually permitted some degree of individual freedom; however, the nation now has a political system in which the ruler has absolute power and attempts to control all aspects of society. Which statement about this nation is accurate?

A. It has moved from totalitarianism to authoritarianism.

B. It has moved from authoritarianism to totalitarianism.

C. It has moved from totalitarianism to representative democracy.

D. It has moved from representative democracy to authoritarianism.

______ **8.** When President Barack Obama appointed a board to review and resolve a railroad dispute in 2011, his action demonstrated the close connection between business and

A. society.

B. economics.

C. politicians.

D. government.

______ **9.** Max Weber stated that a political institution must rest on a stable form of

A. power.

B. the nation.

C. tradition.

D. the individual.

______ **10.** Which is an example of a totalitarian state?

A. Iraq in 2012

B. France in 1955

C. Germany in 1933

D. United States in 1970

NAME ______________________________ DATE ____________________ CLASS ____________

Lesson Quiz 13-2

networks

Political and Economic Institutions

DIRECTIONS: Completion Write the word or phrase that correctly completes each statement.

1. The power elite exercise power. This sentence most accurately reflects the belief of a person who holds the ____________________.

2. For most people in the United States, the leading source of political and public-affairs information is ____________________.

3. The two major models of political power are pluralism and ____________________.

4. An example of a non-economic interest group is ____________________.

5. The functionalist theory of power distribution assumes that power in the United States is held among various ____________________.

DIRECTIONS: Multiple Choice Indicate the answer choice that best completes the statement or answers the question.

________ **6.** Which is a major agent of political socialization for most people?

A. economists
B. family members
C. politicians
D. social scientists

________ **7.** The functionalist perspective regarding models of political power believes that power is exercised by

A. economic and public policies.
B. mass media and social celebrities.
C. national political and military leaders.
D. bargaining and compromising interest groups.

________ **8.** The majority of attitudes and beliefs expressed as political opinions are gained through a learning process called political

A. elitism.
B. profiling.
C. economics.
D. socialization.

________ **9.** In the United States, voter turnout

A. is lower than that of most other countries.
B. is about the same as that of most other countries.
C. is much higher than that or most other countries.
D. has changed more significantly during the past decade than that of other countries.

________ **10.** The conflict perspective regarding models of political power states that the basis for public policy decisions lies in

A. corporate leadership.
B. goals and values being shared by members of the general public.
C. preferences of the power elite.
D. government leaders offering close and careful attention to political supporters.

NAME ______________________ DATE ______________ CLASS __________

Lesson Quiz 13-3

networks

Political and Economic Institutions

DIRECTIONS: True/False In the blank, indicate whether the statement is true (T) or false (F).

_______ **1.** Capitalism is an economic system founded on the right of individuals to profit from their labors.

_______ **2.** The United States Constitution clearly provides a role for the national government in the promotion of a sound economy.

_______ **3.** An oligopoly is a company that has control over the production or distribution of a product or service.

_______ **4.** When the former Soviet Union no longer exerted influence over Czechoslovakian politics, Czechoslovakia moved from private to public ownership of businesses.

_______ **5.** Social philosopher Adam Smith stated that capitalism would result in the public receiving high-quality goods and services at reasonable prices.

DIRECTIONS: Multiple Choice Indicate the answer choice that best completes the statement or answers the question.

_______ **6.** In 2008, the U.S. government promised $15 billion to automakers and $700 billion to financial institutions. This was an example of

A. loan guarantees.
B. monopolistic indicators.
C. deviation from legal standards.
D. technology support through costs.

_______ **7.** Socialism was founded on the belief that means of production should be

A. controlled wholly by the people.
B. primarily controlled by government.
C. essentially controlled by special officials elected by the people.
D. controlled partially by the government and partially by the people.

_______ **8.** Which best describes the economic system of most nations?

A. capitalist
B. socialist
C. monopolistic
D. mixed

_______ **9.** What has been the outcome of strict socialist systems?

A. They fail to eliminate income inequalities.
B. They lack ruling members of government.
C. They result in sustained economic growth.
D. They work to meet relevant needs of business.

_______ **10.** Capitalism is founded on the sanctity of

A. societal strata.
B. private property.
C. voting registration.
D. government officials.

NAME ______________________________ DATE ____________________ CLASS ____________

Lesson Quiz 13-4

networks

Political and Economic Institutions

DIRECTIONS: True/False In the blank, indicate whether the statement is true (T) or false (F).

_______ **1.** U.S. corporations dominate the American economic system and influence economies of nations throughout the world.

_______ **2.** A corporation is an organization owned by people who have unlimited control over the corporation's business.

_______ **3.** Those who defend multinationals state that these corporations provide developing countries with technology.

_______ **4.** Conglomerates are networks of related businesses operating under multiple corporate umbrellas.

_______ **5.** Major corporate officials generally have little influence over government decisions.

DIRECTIONS: Multiple Choice Indicate the answer choice that best completes the statement or answers the question.

_______ **6.** Lee is a partial owner of a corporation that runs a business, and the corporation owes millions of dollars. Which statement about liability for the debt would be accurate in most situations?

A. Lee's personal funds are safe from the debt.
B. The debt will be paid primarily from Lee's personal funds.
C. The debt will be paid from Lee's personal funds and business funds.
D. Lee's personal funds and the business funds will be safe from the debt.

_______ **7.** Which is an example of an interlocking directorate? The head of corporation A

A. makes arrangements with the head of Corporation B for the two corporations to merge.
B. refuses to communicate with the head of Corporation B.
C. files court papers to separate business from the head of Corporation B.
D. and the head of Corporation B sit on one another's corporate boards.

_______ **8.** In 2010, for the first time in history, the U.S. Supreme Court permitted corporations to exert influence over the political system through spending profits on

A. political advertising.
B. investment in essential business equipment.
C. paying government officials for favors.
D. social programs.

_______ **9.** A corporation is owned by

A. its nation's government.
B. local interest groups.
C. its shareholders.
D. local businesses.

_______ **10.** It is difficult for less economically developed nations to establish new companies that can compete with multinationals because

A. the less economically developed nations lack the motivation of multinationals.
B. multinationals dominate the industries in less economically developed nations.
C. the less economically developed nations lack raw materials the multinationals are seeking.
D. multinationals make certain that foreign markets are closed to less economically developed nations.

NAME ______________________ DATE ____________ CLASS ____________

Lesson Quiz 13-5

networks

Political and Economic Institutions

DIRECTIONS: Matching Match each item with the correct statement below.

_______ **1.** contingent employment

_______ **2.** peripheral tier

_______ **3.** downsizing

_______ **4.** tertiary sector

_______ **5.** occupation

A. part of the economy that provides services

B. category of jobs that involves similar activities at different work locations

C. the hiring of part-time, short-term workers

D. part of the job structure composed of smaller, less-profitable firms

E. process by which a company reduce its workforce

DIRECTIONS: Multiple Choice Indicate the answer choice that best completes the statement or answers the question.

_______ **6.** Which of the following jobs would be in the primary sector? A(an)

A. worker in a phone factory
B. cashier in a clothing store
C. insurance salesperson
D. vegetable farmer

_______ **7.** A person holding which job would most likely work in a core-tier firm?

A. a rancher
B. a pharmacist
C. a sales clerk
D. a restaurant server

_______ **8.** From the 1970s–1990s, downsizing

A. rose dramatically.
B. rose and then declined.
C. declined slightly.
D. remained almost the same.

_______ **9.** What was the primary reason for the increase in unskilled jobs moving from the United States to other parts of the world during the recent past?

A. American workers refused to continue to do these jobs.
B. The wages were lower for the same work in some other nations.
C. Americans wanted greater variety in the jobs they sought in the workplace.
D. There were many people in other nations who were able to do these jobs.

_______ **10.** Which best describes the fastest-growing job type in the secondary sector in the United States since World War II?

A. blue collar
B. agricultural
C. white collar
D. environmental

NAME ______________________ DATE ______________________ CLASS ______________________

Chapter 13 Test, Form A

networks

Political and Economic Institutions

DIRECTIONS: Matching Match each item with the correct statement below.

_______ **1.** power elite

_______ **2.** capitalism

_______ **3.** primary sector

_______ **4.** economic institution

_______ **5.** core tier

_______ **6.** conglomerate

_______ **7.** oligopoly

_______ **8.** charismatic authority

_______ **9.** multinationals

_______ **10.** pluralism

A. combination of companies that control the production or distribution of a product or service

B. includes jobs with large firms holding dominant positions within their industries

C. set of organizations that determine how goods and services are produced and distributed

D. network of unrelated businesses operating under one umbrella

E. system in which political decisions are made as a result of bargaining and compromise among special-interest groups

F. firms based in highly industrialized societies with operating facilities throughout the world

G. economic system based on private ownership of property and the pursuit of profit

H. unified group of military, corporate, and government leaders

I. part of an economy producing goods directly from the natural environment

J. arises from a leader's personal characteristics

DIRECTIONS: Multiple Choice Indicate the answer choice that best completes the statement or answers the question.

_______ **11.** During a beginning study of sociology, it is appropriate to think of politics as the exercise of power and economics as the distribution of

A. society.
B. behavior.
C. resources.
D. government.

_______ **12.** Which is at the opposite end of the political spectrum from democracy?

A. totalitarianism
B. authoritarianism
C. traditional authority
D. charismatic authority

_______ **13.** In the United States, which is generally required if a candidate is to have a chance of winning a state or national office?

A. endorsement of a major political party
B. spotless voting record in the jurisdiction
C. prior service in the elected position being sought
D. attitudes similar to those of current governing officials

_______ **14.** The environmental lobby best exemplifies a(n)

A. public policy.

B. mass media influence.

C. interest group.

D. power of the voting public.

_______ **15.** Which of the following people works in the primary sector?

A. a farmer who raises chickens

B. a baker

C. a website developer

D. a dentist

_______ **16.** What did eighteenth-century Scottish social philosopher Adam Smith state was the regulator of economy?

A. self-interest

B. mixed economic systems

C. monopolies

D. state-owned small businesses

_______ **17.** Which of the following would be a legal interlocking directorate?

A. a food supply corporation and a grocery store corporation.

B. a restaurant corporation and an auto manufacturing corporation.

C. a cell phone corporation and a software development corporation.

D. a computer monitor sales corporation and a keyboard sales corporation.

_______ **18.** If all the top political and economic units in the world were combined—and then the top 100 units were chosen—about what percentage of the top 100 units would be multinational corporations instead of countries?

A. 25% **C.** 75%

B. 45% **D.** 95%

_______ **19.** Which is an example of a secondary-sector job?

A. rancher **C.** real estate agent

B. bank teller **D.** steel factory worker

_______ **20.** What type of practice was exemplified by Microsoft Corporation's insistence that manufacturers include only its Internet browser on their computers?

A. monopolistic **C.** capitalistic

B. oligopolistic **D.** socialistic

Political and Economic Institutions

DIRECTIONS: Essays Answer the following questions on a separate sheet of paper.

21. Do you think democracy and civil liberties have been increasing in the world during the past decade? Support your answer with specific examples.

22. Suppose you owned a large business and you were considering whether to form a corporation. Discuss at least two pros and two cons you would consider while making the decision. Explain whether you think corporations should be more or less strictly controlled by governmental regulations.

Workers by Occupational Category, 2010

Occupational Category	Percent of Total	Percent Male	Percent Female
Management, professional, and related occupations	37.2	48.5	51.5
Service occupations	24.0	37.1	62.9
Sales and office occupations	17.7	43.2	56.8
Natural resources, construction, and maintenance occupations	9.4	95.4	4.6
Production, transportation, and material-moving occupations	11.6	88.8	21.2

Source: U.S. Census Bureau, *Statistical Abstract of the United States: 2012*

23. Look at the data in the table. Why do you think there is such a large disparity in the percentages of *Female* and *Male* workers in the *Natural resources, construction, and maintenance occupations* category? Do you think this disparity is likely to change in time? Explain your answer.

Chapter 13 Test, Form B

networks

Political and Economic Institutions

DIRECTIONS: Matching Match each item with the correct statement below.

_______ **1.** deviation

_______ **2.** political socialization

_______ **3.** coercion

_______ **4.** corporations

_______ **5.** interest groups

_______ **6.** interlocking directorates

_______ **7.** downsizing

_______ **8.** representative democracy

_______ **9.** secondary sector

_______ **10.** monopolies

A. entities organized for the purpose of influencing political decision making

B. system that uses elected officials to fulfill majority wishes

C. results in heads of corporations sitting on one another's boards

D. informal and formal processes by which a person develops opinions

E. companies that have control over the production or distribution of a product or service

F. a move away from that which is expected

G. control through force

H. the part of the economy engaged in manufacturing goods

I. organizations owned by shareholders that dominate the American economic system

J. process by which companies reduce their workforces

DIRECTIONS: Multiple Choice Indicate the answer choice that best completes the statement or answers the question.

_______ **11.** Dr. Martin Luther King, Jr., inspired many people through his personality and the strength of his ideas. Which term identifies the form of authority this exemplifies?

A. legitimate
B. traditional
C. charismatic
D. rational-legal

_______ **12.** Which form of government arose in Russia due to opportunities created by the collapse of communism and the end of the Cold War?

A. republican
B. democratic
C. totalitarian
D. authoritarian

_______ **13.** For most people in the United States, which is the leading source of political and public-affairs information?

A. mass media
B. interest groups
C. economic indicators
D. congressional lobbies

Chapter 13 Test, Form B *cont.*

networks

Political and Economic Institutions

_______ **14.** Which most limits the range of candidates in major U.S. elections?

A. elitism
B. pluralism
C. political parties
D. regional locations

_______ **15.** Which was a major factor in the process of members of the Polish population forming business relationships, learning about capitalist methods, and importing goods during the period of Soviet communist domination?

A. voting rights
B. overall freedom
C. international travel
D. property ownership

_______ **16.** Which correctly reflects a position of social philosopher Adam Smith?

A. Over-regulation by government is inevitable.
B. It is sometimes necessary for the state to intervene to prevent abuses by businesses.
C. Government should take a hands-off approach regarding the economy.
D. A combination of private ownership of property and the pursuit of profit creates disadvantages for the state and society.

_______ **17.** Of these features, which would be considered a negative aspect in selecting a corporate structure as a way to organize your business?

A. avoidance of debt
B. limited shareholder liability
C. lack of direct voice in daily operations
D. strong influence of officials on government

_______ **18.** Suppose you knew only this fact about a corporation: It has operating facilities in the United States and France. What would you know for certain about this corporation?

A. It has interlocking directorates.
B. It is a conglomerate.
C. It has few economic advantages.
D. It is multinational.

_______ **19.** If you were discussing people who fish to make a living, you would most likely be discussing the

A. core tier.
B. primary sector.
C. peripheral tier.
D. secondary sector.

_______ **20.** Shipping companies often hire additional workers for the busy holiday season, but these jobs are scheduled to end in January. Which of the following best describes this type of employment?

A. specialty
B. contingent
C. downsizing
D. administrative

Political and Economic Institutions

DIRECTIONS: Essays Answer the following questions on a separate sheet of paper.

21. Compare and contrast totalitarianism and authoritarianism. Why do you think the United States is not governed by either of these forms of authority?

22. Some people feel that monopolies are efficient and fair, while others feel that monopolies create unfair control of a particular industry or service. Explain your position on this issue in an essay. Support your response with examples.

"Perhaps most importantly, respondents noted that *The Daily Show* was more user-friendly than the other new sources mentioned in the survey. . . . The complexity of political news stories, and the generally unfamiliar nature of the rhetoric and concepts employed there, make it difficult for relatively unsophisticated viewers to get a good understanding of the topic at hand. Traditionally partisanship has been used to simplify these stories, making it clear which side is right, and which wrong, but among young people alienated from the parties, this isn't necessary an option. While many of the respondents voiced this concern when describing other media sources, saying that they didn't understand them, or that they were talking about obscure topics, things that no one really cares about, or has time for, such comments were missing from descriptions of *The Daily Show* and its viewers. It was not uncommon for a typical viewer to be described as someone 'that does not know anything about politics.' This is a political news program that anyone can watch and understand."

—Dan Cassino, from *Consuming Politics: Jon Stewart, Branding, and the Youth Vote in America*, 2009.

23. President Thomas Jefferson believed that well-informed people can be trusted with their own government, and when things go wrong, they can be relied upon to set them right by voting. How would people have been "well-informed" in the early eighteen hundreds compared with today? How does the quote above compare with Jefferson's thoughts about a well-informed voter?

networks Chapter 13 Test, Form B cont.

Political and Economic Institutions

NAME ________________________ DATE ____________ CLASS ____________

Lesson Quiz 14-1

networks

Religion

DIRECTIONS: True/False In the blank, indicate whether the statement is true (T) or false (F).

________ **1.** It is essential for sociologists to remain objective as they study religion.

________ **2.** According to Émile Durkheim, it is rare for societies to distinguish between the sacred and the profane.

________ **3.** Karl Marx stated that religion was used to overthrow the group in power.

________ **4.** Symbolic interactionism holds that people create symbolic meaning from their religious beliefs, rituals, and ideas.

________ **5.** Functionalists state that an important function of religion is to provide people with a sense of unity and belonging.

DIRECTIONS: Multiple Choice Indicate the answer choice that best completes the statement or answers the question.

________ **6.** When a sociologist says that an object is profane, he or she means that it is

A. secular.

B. evil.

C. unclean.

D. sacred.

________ **7.** What is the focus of functionalists toward religion?

A. Functionalists examine the contributions of religion to society.

B. Functionalists examine the importance of symbols to religion.

C. Functionalists examine the power structure of the elite in religion.

D. Functionalists examine the fundamental nature of religions in society.

________ **8.** John Calvin believed the purpose of life was to glorify God on Earth through

A. public service.

B. church formation.

C. occupational calling.

D. investment avoidance.

________ **9.** Max Weber stated there was a link between Protestantism and

A. despotism.

B. Buddhism.

C. capitalism.

D. Hinduism.

________ **10.** Which perspective states the conclusion that religion is used by the most powerful to justify their economic, political, and social advantages?

A. conflict theory

B. functionalist theory

C. symbolic interactionism

D. separation of church and state

NAME ________________ DATE ________________ CLASS ________________

Lesson Quiz 14-2

networks

Religion

DIRECTIONS: Completion Write the word or phrase that correctly completes each statement.

1. According to sociologists, a life-encompassing religious organization to which all members of a society belong is a ________________.

2. Formed in 1693 and led by a Swiss bishop, the religion that stated that only people who could be successful in their religious beliefs should be a part of the community, and all others should be disregarded and shunned is ________________.

3. According to sociologists, most American religious organizations such as Reform Judaism, Episcopalian, Presbyterian, Baptist, Roman Catholic, and Methodist are not churches, but are actually ________________.

4. Practicing sexual abstinence before marriage, or opposing or supporting capital punishment are examples of religious ________________.

5. Assume that a small group of churches within a large Protestant religious organization believe their organization is no longer acting according to the beliefs of its founders, so they break away and create a new organization. This new organization is an example of a ________________.

DIRECTIONS: Multiple Choice Indicate the answer choice that best completes the statement or answers the question.

_______ **6.** Which of the following is the most accurate statement regarding denominations?

A. They are closely tied to the government.
B. Their leaders are often politically active.
C. They are rarely accepted as legitimate in society.
D. They are generally prohibited from competing for members.

_______ **7.** Pilgrims who landed at Plymouth Rock are an example of what sociologists refer to as a

A. ritual. **C.** sect.
B. cult. **D.** denomination.

_______ **8.** All new religious movements (NRMs) can accurately be characterized as

A. forming cults. **C.** engaging in extreme behavior.
B. coming from sects. **D.** being drawn from existing religious tradition.

_______ **9.** The four basic types of religious organizations identified by sociologists are

A. new religious movement, religiosity, church, and denomination.
B. church, ritual, sect, and denomination.
C. sect, experience, ritual, and religiosity.
D. denomination, new religious movement, sect, and church.

_______ **10.** The sociological term that identifies types of religious attitudes and behavior people display in their everyday lives is

A. religiosity. **C.** religioethical.
B. religion rigor. **D.** religious affirmation.

Lesson Quiz 14-3

networks

Religion

DIRECTIONS: True/False In the blank, indicate whether the statement is true (T) or false (F).

_______ **1.** Religious faiths can be examined and analyzed using major social characteristics such as class and political tendencies.

_______ **2.** The Framers of the U.S. Constitution often raised arguments against the practice of religious faith.

_______ **3.** The political and religious affiliations of people in the United States are often related to the level of education the people have attained.

_______ **4.** Regardless of their religious affiliation, most African Americans identify with the Republican Party.

_______ **5.** Religious fundamentalism has been waning in the United States.

DIRECTIONS: Multiple Choice Indicate the answer choice that best completes the statement or answers the question.

_______ **6.** In colonial America, formal education was originally a function of

A. delegates to the Constitutional Convention.
B. teachers brought in from England.
C. the government.
D. religious organizations.

_______ **7.** Which statement regarding religion in the United States is most accurate?

A. Few people in the nation believe in life after death.
B. Secularization in the nation has been steadily increasing.
C. Religious life in the nation has become less diverse.
D. The proportion of people in the nation that belong to a church, synagogue, or mosque has increased.

_______ **8.** Which accurately describes neo-Pentacostalism?

A. It believes in a direct gift from the Holy Spirit.
B. Its members must refrain from speaking in tongues.
C. It demands that its followers give up fundamentalism.
D. It refuses to recognize the charismatic movement.

_______ **9.** Teaching "intelligent design" in public schools has been ruled unconstitutional by courts in the United States, because it is a form of

A. evolution.
B. pure science.
C. creationism.
D. gene therapy.

_______ **10.** The temperance movement in the United States, which resulted in outlawing the sale of alcohol during the 1920s and the 1930s was led by

A. Protestants.
B. Catholics.
C. Muslims.
D. Buddhists.

NAME ______________________________ DATE ______________ CLASS __________

Chapter 14 Test, Form A

networks

Religion

DIRECTIONS: Matching Match each item with the correct statement below.

_______ **1.** secularization

_______ **2.** profane

_______ **3.** denomination

_______ **4.** religiosity

_______ **5.** Protestant ethic

_______ **6.** religious affiliation

_______ **7.** belief of Karl Marx

_______ **8.** religion

_______ **9.** sect

_______ **10.** church

A. values, norms, and beliefs that stressed hard work and discipline

B. religious organization characterized by close state ties

C. a reason used to explain political affiliation

D. a group that sees its role as reforming a religious faith

E. unified system of beliefs and practices concerned with sacred things

F. religious behaviors displayed in a person's everyday life

G. non-sacred aspects of life

H. the process through which the sacred loses influence over society

I. religion justifies economic and social inequalities

J. one of several religious organizations that most members of society accept as legitimate

DIRECTIONS: Multiple Choice Indicate the answer choice that best completes the statement or answers the question.

_______ **11.** Sociologists limit their study of religion to those items that can be

A. observed.

B. explained.

C. described.

D. experienced.

_______ **12.** Émile Durkheim believed that the essential function of religion was to provide social solidarity and cohesiveness through the use of ceremonies and

A. clear ethics.

B. historical icons.

C. sacred symbols.

D. legitimate leaders.

_______ **13.** The key figure in Buddhism is

A. Jesus.

B. Gurū Nānak.

C. Muhammad.

D. Siddhartha Gautama.

______ **14.** Jo believes that due to karma, "what goes around comes around." Because she has lived her life as a kind, thoughtful human being, she thinks her next life will be a good one. Jo most likely believes in

A. Islam.

B. Sikhism.

C. Judaism.

D. Hinduism.

______ **15.** Richard just read an article about a faith followed by some people in his town. The faith was recently started by someone looking for a belief system that did not follow traditions already established in society. The faith Richard was reading about can best be identified as a

A. new religious movement.

B. shunned community.

C. denomination.

D. church.

______ **16.** Which religious organization is often given as an example of a sect?

A. Amish

B. Baptists

C. atheists

D. Protestants

______ **17.** Religiosity refers to

A. setting certain objects aside and treating them as sacred.

B. the increasing strength of the charismatic movement.

C. the increasing fundamentalism of many denominations.

D. how your religion affects your behavior and attitudes in daily life.

______ **18.** The views of religious fundamentalists most closely align with the views of

A. Marxists.

B. practicing atheists.

C. Darwinists.

D. conservative politicians.

______ **19.** Strict fundamentalists would most likely request public school instruction regarding

A. evolution.

B. the Big Bang theory.

C. intelligent design.

D. Newton's laws of motion.

_______ **20.** Which best describes the number of religious denominations in the United States?

A. tens

B. hundreds

C. thousands

D. millions

DIRECTIONS: Essays Answer the following questions on a separate sheet of paper.

21. Distinguish among the ways functionalism, conflict theory, and symbolic interactionism interpret religion. Explain which perspective you believe makes the most sense.

22. What is religiosity? Discuss the five dimensions of religiosity. Explain which you believe is the most important.

> "In the beginning, and to some extent ever since, Americans have interpreted their history as having religious meaning. They saw themselves as being a 'people' in the classical and biblical sense of the word. They hoped they were a people of God."
>
> —from *The Broken Covenant* by Robert Bellah, 1975

23. The words in this quote were published in 1975. Explain whether you think the quote remains accurate and still holds true today.

NAME ______________________ DATE ______________ CLASS ________

Chapter 14 Test, Form B

networks

Religion

DIRECTIONS: Matching Match each item with the correct statement below.

_______ **1.** Protestant ethic

_______ **2.** sacred

_______ **3.** religiosity

_______ **4.** church

_______ **5.** fundamentalism

_______ **6.** spirit of capitalism

_______ **7.** sect

_______ **8.** new religious movements

_______ **9.** theological

_______ **10.** monotheism

A. religious organization that arises out of a desire to reform an exiting religious organization

B. a life-encompassing system of beliefs and practices to which all members of a society belong

C. an obligation to reinvest money in business, rather than spend it

D. religious organizations whose characteristics are not drawn from existing religious traditions within a society

E. belief in one god

F. things and ideas that are set apart and given a special meaning that extends beyond immediate existence

G. ways in which people express their religious interests and convictions

H. resistance of secularization and the rigid adherence to traditional religious beliefs, rituals, and doctrines

I. set of values, norms, beliefs, and attitudes that stress hard work, thrift, and self-discipline

J. relating to the study of religious belief

DIRECTIONS: Multiple Choice Indicate the answer choice that best completes the statement or answers the question.

_______ **11.** The earliest evidence of religious customs and taboos has been traced back as far as

A. 100 B.C.

B. 1,000 B.C.

C. 5,000 B.C.

D. 50,000 B.C.

_______ **12.** Oscar believes that religion is used by the most powerful people in his city to justify their lavish lifestyles, huge bank accounts, and connections to the town's mayor. Oscar's viewpoint most closely aligns with

A. the functionalist perspective.

B. the conflict theory perspective.

C. the symbolic interactionism perspective.

D. a mix of functionalist, conflict theory, and symbolic interactionism perspectives.

_______ **13.** If a class is studying the Protestant ethic, the study will most likely include the work of

A. Siddhartha Gautama.

B. Peter Berger.

C. John Calvin.

D. Abraham.

_______ **14.** Which is an accurate statement regarding the views of Max Weber and Karl Marx?

A. Weber believed that religion sometimes encourages social change, while Marx believed that religion works against social change.

B. Marx believed that religion sometimes encourages social change, while Weber believed that religion works against social change.

C. Weber and Marx both believed that religion sometimes encourages social change.

D. Marx and Weber both believed that religion works against social change.

_______ **15.** Which is the best example of a ritual?

A. knowledge of sacred texts

B. belief in one god

C. telling the truth regardless of its consequences

D. attending a religious ceremony weekly

_______ **16.** The sociological definition of *church* differs from the one commonly used in American society. When most Americans mention churches, they are actually referring to something sociologists call

A. sects.

B. norms.

C. cults.

D. denominations.

_______ **17.** Which dimension of religiosity is the most difficult to measure?

A. belief

B. intellectual

C. experience

D. consequences

_______ **18.** The sacred loses influence over society through the process of

A. secularization.

B. universality.

C. diversity.

D. tradition.

_______ **19.** Which describes weekly attendance at religious services in the United States from the late 1930s to 2010?

A. It increased.

B. It remained essentially the same.

C. It declined.

D. It decreased dramatically, but then increased substantially.

_______ **20.** Which is an example of a polytheistic religion?

A. Judaism

B. Hinduism

C. Christianity

D. Islam

DIRECTIONS: Essays Answer the following questions on a separate sheet of paper.

21. The particular items thought of as sacred can vary from one culture to the next. Provide at least one example and explain whether you think this makes sense.

22. Why is it important for sociologists to be objective when they study and report on religion? Explain whether you believe that a sociologist can be truly objective and not interject personal faith beliefs into study and analysis.

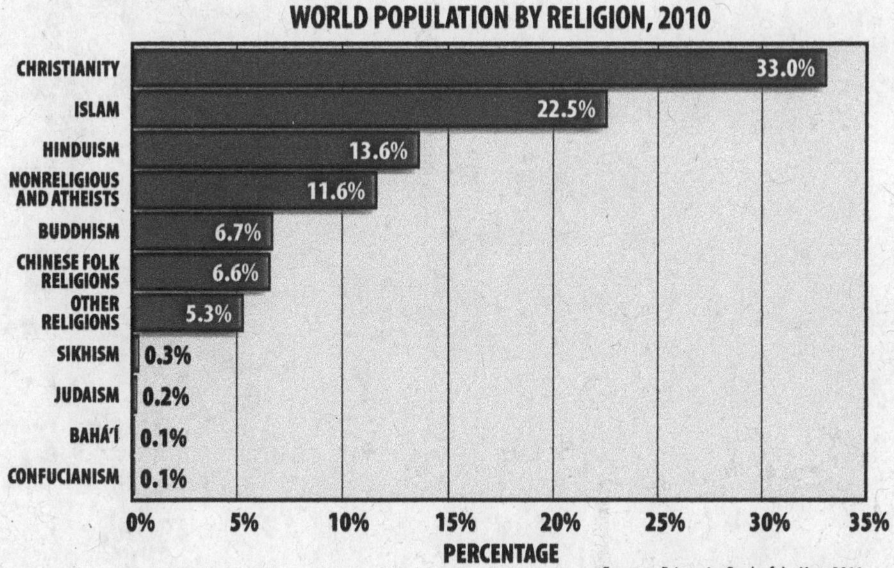

Source: *Britannica Book of the Year, 2011.*

23. The graph shows the number of adherents to various religions as a percentage of the population of the world. However, particular religious populations are not evenly distributed in all countries of the world. Discuss one way this uneven distribution can be considered a positive social force and one way it can be considered a negative force.

Religion

WORLD POPULATION BY RELIGION, 2010

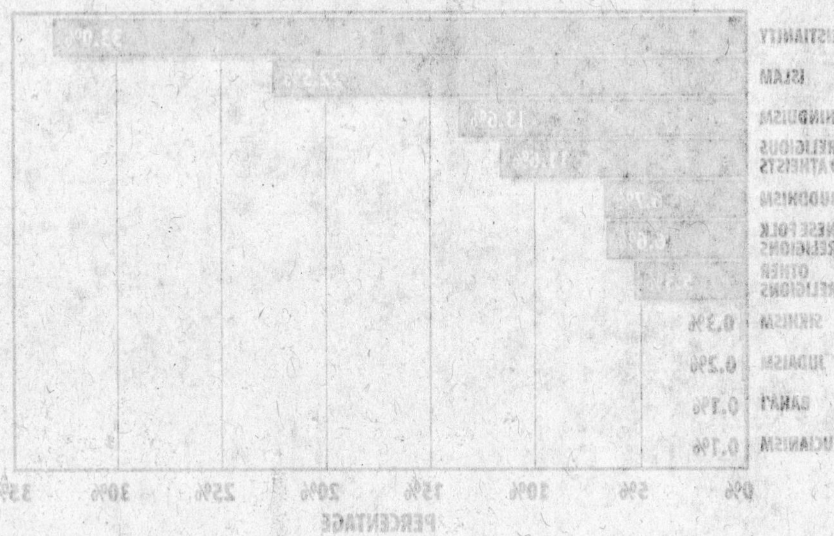

NAME ______________________________ DATE ______________________ CLASS ____________

Lesson Quiz 15-1

networks

Population and Urbanization

DIRECTIONS: Matching Match each item with the correct statement below.

_______ **1.** fertility

_______ **2.** lifespan

_______ **3.** demography

_______ **4.** migration

_______ **5.** fecundity

A. scientific study of population

B. actual number of children a woman has

C. potential number of children a woman can have

D. most advanced age to which humans can survive

E. movement of people from one geographic area to another

DIRECTIONS: Multiple Choice Indicate the answer choice that best completes the statement or answers the question.

_______ **6.** Selma's family moved from a country farm to a large busy city. This is an example of

A. rural-to-urban migration.

B. gross migration rate.

C. urban-to-rural migration.

D. net migration rate.

_______ **7.** Which statement regarding crude birthrate is accurate?

A. It is of little interest to demographers.

B. It is essentially the same from one country to the next.

C. It is the annual number of live births per 1,000 members of a population.

D. It is calculated by dividing the total population of a nation by the annual number of live births and multiplying that number by 100.

_______ **8.** Which identifies the potential number of children that could be born if every woman reproduced as often as biology allowed?

A. fertility rate

B. demography

C. life expectancy

D. fecundity

_______ **9.** A group of people living in a particular place at a specified time can best be identified by the term

A. census.

B. migration.

C. structure.

D. population.

_______ **10.** Which best explains why many different types of businesses wish to acquire demographic information?

A. to provide statistics for their customers

B. to tailor their goods and services to make higher sales

C. to examine earlier patterns of moves between cities

D. to determine the difference between birthrates and death rates

NAME ______________________ DATE ______________ CLASS __________

Lesson Quiz 15-2

networks

Population and Urbanization

DIRECTIONS: True/False In the blank, indicate whether the statement is true (T) or false (F).

______ **1.** Several organizations have counted all the people in the world.

______ **2.** The quality of census data is generally uniform and reliable.

______ **3.** The demographic transition theory states that population growth is a function of the level of economic development in a country.

______ **4.** Population grows exponentially.

______ **5.** The term *replacement level* refers to the birthrate at which a couple replaces themselves without adding to the population.

DIRECTIONS: Multiple Choice Indicate the answer choice that best completes the statement or answers the question.

______ **6.** Which answer best explains the doubling time of the world's population?

A. It is getting shorter.
B. It is getting longer.
C. It is remaining the same.
D. It is rising sharply, but in time will fall substantially.

______ **7.** What did economist Thomas Malthus predict would happen as a result of unchecked population growth?

A. The supply of food would keep up with population growth.
B. The education rate of the poor would increase.
C. The food supply would be exceeded by population growth.
D. In time, people would naturally choose to have fewer children.

______ **8.** Which best explains what will happen when the world reaches zero-population growth?

A. Births will be balanced by deaths.
B. Deaths will increase by three times the current scale.
C. Births will decrease in most countries.
D. The rate of deaths and births will cease to be relevant.

______ **9.** Family planning is also known as

A. governmental effort to control the birthrate.
B. voluntary use of population control methods.
C. control of population through national programs.
D. decline of the birthrate below general control norms.

______ **10.** The purpose of a population pyramid is to depict the

A. migration rates of a population.
B. births and deaths within a population.
C. age and sex composition of a population.
D. marriages and divorces within a population.

NAME ______________________ DATE ______________ CLASS __________

networks

Lesson Quiz 15-3

Population and Urbanization

DIRECTIONS: Completion Write the word or phrase that correctly completes each statement.

1. A dense and permanent concentration of people living in a limited geographic area who earn their living primarily through non-agricultural activities is a ______________.

2. The major changes in transportation, agriculture, commerce, and industry that began in the 1700s are referred to as the ______________.

3. During the eighteenth century, machinery and equipment makers located their plants next to factories. In turn, all of these businesses attracted shops, innkeepers, and others. As services increased, more people were attracted, thus maintaining the process of ______________.

4. The concentration of people in need of public services without the tax base being able to-generate enough funds to provide for them is known as the ______________.

5. Many of the first urban settlements were established after people learned how to cultivate plants and domesticate animals. This period is known as the ______________.

DIRECTIONS: Multiple Choice Indicate the answer choice that best completes the statement or answers the question.

_______ **6.** Professional developers, landlords, and middle-class home buyers are working in a low-income area near Jan's school. They are renovating apartment buildings. This is an example of

A. gentrification.
B. over-urbanization.
C. suburbanization.
D. under-utilization.

_______ **7.** From 1800 to the mid-1980s, the number of urban dwellers

A. increased 500 times.
B. decreased by half.
C. increased 100 times.
D. decreased by one-third.

_______ **8.** Most of the growth of urban areas in less developed countries before the turn of the century occurred through

A. colonial expansion.
B. increased educational opportunities.
C. increased population growth.
D. the effects of numerous wars.

_______ **9.** Julio's family moved from a city to the suburbs. He told his new friends that the family's new shopping area looks very much like a suburban version of the urban downtown near his old home. This shopping area near his new home can best be described as a(an)

A. economic gathering.
B. purchase village.
C. buying crescent.
D. edge city.

_______ **10.** Which statement regarding the development of cities is accurate?

A. The first cities were small by modern standards.
B. The first cities appeared approximately two thousand years ago.
C. A surplus food supply is not important in the rate of urbanization.
D. In ancient times, a large portion of the world's population was concentrated in cities.

Lesson Quiz 15-4

networks

Population and Urbanization

DIRECTIONS: True/False In the blank, indicate whether the statement is true (T) or false (F).

_______ **1.** Of the four major theories of city growth, contemporary experts have recognized the multiple-nuclei theory as covering the dynamics of city growth for all cities.

_______ **2.** The most interior portion of a concentric-zone city is the residential zone.

_______ **3.** Every city is unique; however, patterns have been found in the way humans interact within the cities they inhabit.

_______ **4.** Within sector theory, the central business district strongly influences other parts of a city.

_______ **5.** The exact shape of a city is a major issue in sector theory.

DIRECTIONS: Multiple Choice Indicate the answer choice that best completes the statement or answers the question.

_______ **6.** The concentric-zone theory describes city growth in terms of distinctive zones that develop from the

A. suburban areas inward to the city in oval sections.

B. businesses in the city to the homes in the city.

C. farming centers near the city to the city center.

D. central city extending outward in circles.

_______ **7.** Urban ecology can best be described as the study of the relationships between city environments and

A. humans. **C.** animals.

B. water sources. **D.** forested landscape.

_______ **8.** Based on the sector theory, each sector is organized around a major

A. area of homes. **C.** center of business.

B. hub for recreation. **D.** route for transportation.

_______ **9.** Which theory emphasizes the statement that growth in any one area of a city is largely influenced by politics and economics?

A. sector **C.** peripheral

B. concentric-zone **D.** multiple-nuclei

_______ **10.** The peripheral theory focuses on the growth of

A. cities in rings away from a suburban center.

B. suburbs around and away from central cities.

C. urban and rural areas developing in tandem into cities.

D. rural areas reaching gradually into city residential areas.

Chapter 15 Test, Form A

networks

Population and Urbanization

DIRECTIONS: Matching Match each item with the correct statement below.

_______ **1.** exponential growth

_______ **2.** fecundity

_______ **3.** city

_______ **4.** population

_______ **5.** gentrification

_______ **6.** sector theory

_______ **7.** infant mortality rate

_______ **8.** concentric-zone theory

_______ **9.** over-urbanization

_______ **10.** population momentum

A. an important indicator of the health status of a group

B. idea that emphasizes the importance of transportation routes in the process of growth

C. inability to stop expansion immediately because of the previous high rate of increase

D. maximum rate at which women can physically produce children

E. occurs when the amount of increase is added to the base figure at each time period and becomes part of the calculation for the next rise

F. situation in which adequate jobs and housing cannot be supplied for inhabitants

G. development of low-income areas by middle-class home buyers, landlords, and professional developers

H. group of people living in a particular place at a specified time

I. dense and permanent concentration of people living in a specific area and working primarily in non-agricultural jobs

J. idea that describes urban growth in terms of circular areas that grow outward

DIRECTIONS: Multiple Choice Indicate the answer choice that best completes the statement or answers the question.

_______ **11.** Ann Dran had three children. In this situation, the number 3 identifies the sociological concept of

A. fertility.

B. fecundity.

C. total births.

D. crude birthrate.

_______ **12.** Which best describes the number of births in the United States since 1960?

A. It has been primarily increasing.

B. It increased sharply during the 1980s.

C. It has been steadily declining.

D. It decreased during the 1970s, but increased during the 1990s.

Chapter 15 Test, Form A *cont.*

networks

Population and Urbanization

_______ **13.** Which statement regarding world population growth is accurate?

A. A substantial decline in growth is anticipated.

B. Growth during the past 70 years has occurred at approximately the same rate as growth during the preceding 4 million years.

C. Rapid growth is a relatively recent occurrence.

D. Growth during the upcoming 200 years is predicted to occur at about the same rate as growth during the preceding 2 million years.

_______ **14.** As related to population increase, what is happening to doubling time?

A. It is growing shorter.

B. It is expected to grow longer, but then grow shorter.

C. It is growing longer and longer.

D. It is expected to grow shorter, but then grow longer.

_______ **15.** Which statement least closely aligns to Malthus' theory regarding population growth?

A. Improvement in income for the poor is consumed by additional births.

B. Population will exceed the food supply if population increase is left unchecked.

C. Positive population checks include events that increase mortality.

D. The wealthy are unable to exercise preventive population checks.

_______ **16.** The U.S. Census Bureau sets the number of people that defines an urban area at a population of 2,500. Which statement about this number is accurate?

A. It was recently established.

B. For modern times, it has been established as a desirable indicator.

C. It was established shortly after urbanization began.

D. When it was established, population concentrations were relatively large.

_______ **17.** Which factor is necessary for urbanization to occur?

A. a large rural concentration

B. a surplus food supply

C. dwindling city size

D. limiting the number of livestock

_______ **18.** For which basic types of people did early cities provide a setting for consolidating political, military, or religious power?

A. functionaries

B. craftspeople

C. destitute

D. elites

_______ **19.** Which best identifies the shape of areas radiating from the central business district to a city's outskirts, as explained by Homer Hoyt?

A. pie-shaped

B. square shaped

C. circle

D. oval

_______ **20.** Which theory of city growth emphasizes the idea that growth in any one area of a city is largely influenced by politics and economics?

A. concentric zone

B. multiple nuclei

C. peripheral

D. sector

DIRECTIONS: Essays Answer the following questions on a separate sheet of paper.

21. Distinguish between gross migration rate and net migration rate. Explain the purpose of these rates. Provide examples of rural-to-urban migration and urban-to-rural migration in the United States. Explain which you think will be more likely by the year 2025—and explain why.

22. Identify and explain four factors and three processes demographers utilize to study population. Explain which two of these you think are the most important.

"... In the media all you heard were politicians' promises to help CHA [Chicago Housing Authority] tenants forge a better life. On the ground, meanwhile, the lowest-ranking members of society got pushed even lower, thanks to a stingy and neglectful city agency and the constant hustling of the few people in a position to help. In the coming months, the place began to take on the feel of a refugee camp, with every person desperate to secure her own welfare, quite possibly at the expense of a neighbor."

—Sudhir Venkateh, from *Gang Leader for a Day*, 2003

Credit: *Gang Leader for a Day* by Sudhir Venkateh. Copyright © 2008 by Sudhir Venkateh. Used by permission of Penguin Group (USA) Inc.

23. How does the quote make the image of the urban housing project more powerful? Why is the urban housing project a relatively recent phenomenon?

NAME ______________________ DATE ______________ CLASS __________

Chapter 15 Test, Form B

networks

Population and Urbanization

DIRECTIONS: Matching Match each item with the correct statement below.

_______ **1.** lifespan

_______ **2.** fertility

_______ **3.** urban ecology

_______ **4.** census

_______ **5.** suburbanization

_______ **6.** multiple-nuclei theory

_______ **7.** demographic transition theory

_______ **8.** urbanization

_______ **9.** demography

_______ **10.** population control

A. regularly occurring count of a particular population

B. idea that population growth is a function of the level of economic development in a country

C. the most advanced age to which humans can survive

D. attempt by government to restrict the birthrate

E. study of the relationship between humans and city environments

F. scientific study of populations

G. idea that focuses on specific geographic or historical influences on growth

H. loss of population to surrounding areas

I. process by which an increasingly larger portion of the world's population lives in cities

J. actual number of children born to a woman or a population of women

DIRECTIONS: Multiple Choice Indicate the answer choice that best completes the statement or answers the question.

_______ **11.** In explaining fecundity, a sociologist would state the highest realistic fecundity rate from a society as

A. three births per woman.

B. eight births per woman.

C. fifteen births per woman.

D. twenty births per woman.

_______ **12.** Homer Hoyt offered sector theory as a model to explain the growth of cites. Which answer best describes this theory?

A. growth affected by major transportation routes

B. growth that resembles a series of circles

C. growth that focuses on geographic influences

D. growth that focuses on historical influences

_______ **13.** Dana moved from California to Missouri. This is an example of

A. migration.

B. gross migration rate.

C. net.

D. net migration rate.

Chapter 15 Test, Form B *cont.*

networks

Population and Urbanization

______ **14.** Which best describes the way a population increases?

A. through momentum
B. exponentially
C. through doubling
D. linearly

______ **15.** If world population continues to grow at the current growth rate, it is predicted that by 2025, the world's population will be about

A. 5 billion.
B. 8 billion.
C. 11 billion.
D. 14 billion.

______ **16.** Which will most greatly contribute to zero-population growth?

A. population control decreasing
B. population momentum increasing
C. world fertility rate reaching the replacement level
D. family planning that meets compulsory limitation laws

______ **17.** By 2011, about what portion of the world's population lived in urban areas?

A. 26 percent
B. 51 percent
C. 74 percent
D. 93 percent

______ **18.** Which term describes a situation in which a city is unable to supply adequate jobs and housing for its inhabitants?

A. central-city dilemma
B. over-urbanization
C. gentrification
D. suburban

______ **19.** Which theory of city growth is the newest and was developed to address more recent cities?

A. peripheral
B. concentric-zone
C. multiple-nuclei
D. sector

_______ **20.** An urban ecologist would most likely study

A. economists.

B. buildings.

C. politicians.

D. wildlife.

DIRECTIONS: Essays Answer the following questions on a separate sheet of paper.

21. What is the infant mortality rate? Explain whether it is a good indicator of the health status of a group. Explain whether you believe there are other indicators that are also important.

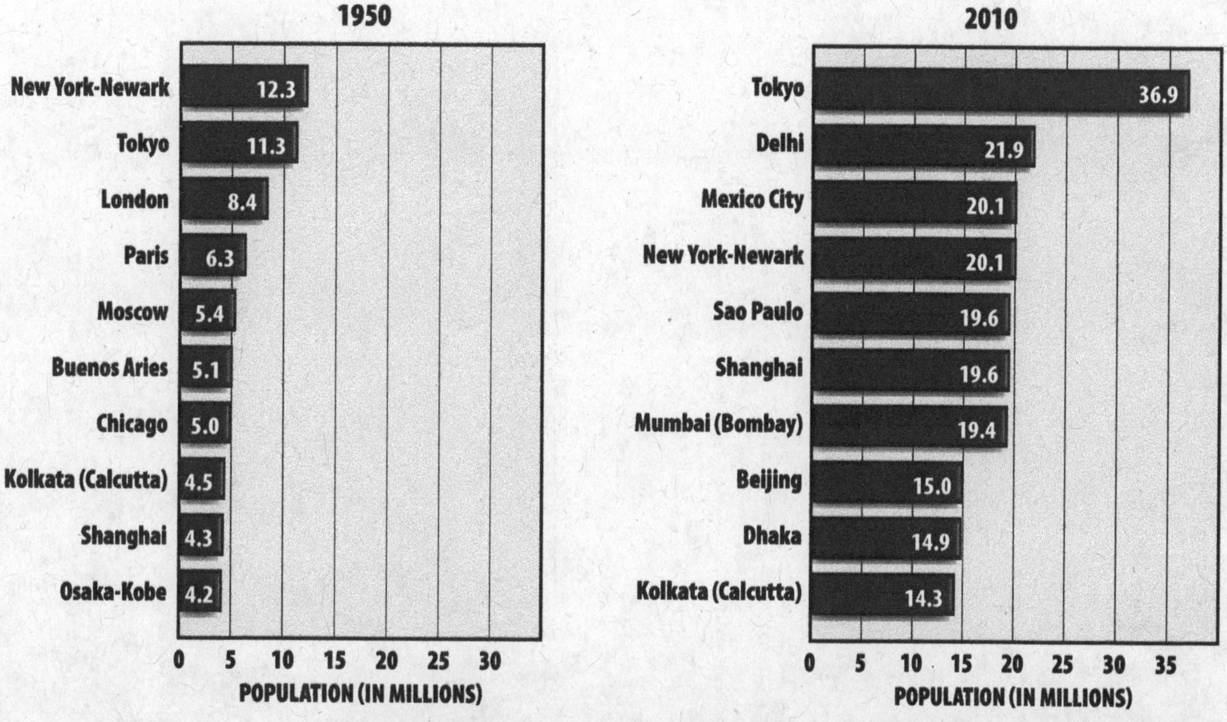

Source: United Nations, Department of Economic and Social Affairs, Population Division, *World Urbanization Prospects: The 2011 Revision*, 2012

22. The graphs above show the population of the 10 largest cities in the world in 1950 and 2010. What change in the position of New York-Newark do you notice? What inferences can you draw about the birthrates, the death rates, and migration rates in a city's population in the 60-year span shown in the graph?

23. Economist Thomas Malthus's study of population growth was first published in 1798. He wrote that population growth, if unchecked, would increase at a faster rate then the supply of available food. A lack of food would thus be a check on an ever-increasing population. What other checks on population growth did Malthus identify? Do you think Malthus was correct in his writings? Why?

Chapter 15 Test, Form B *cont.* networks

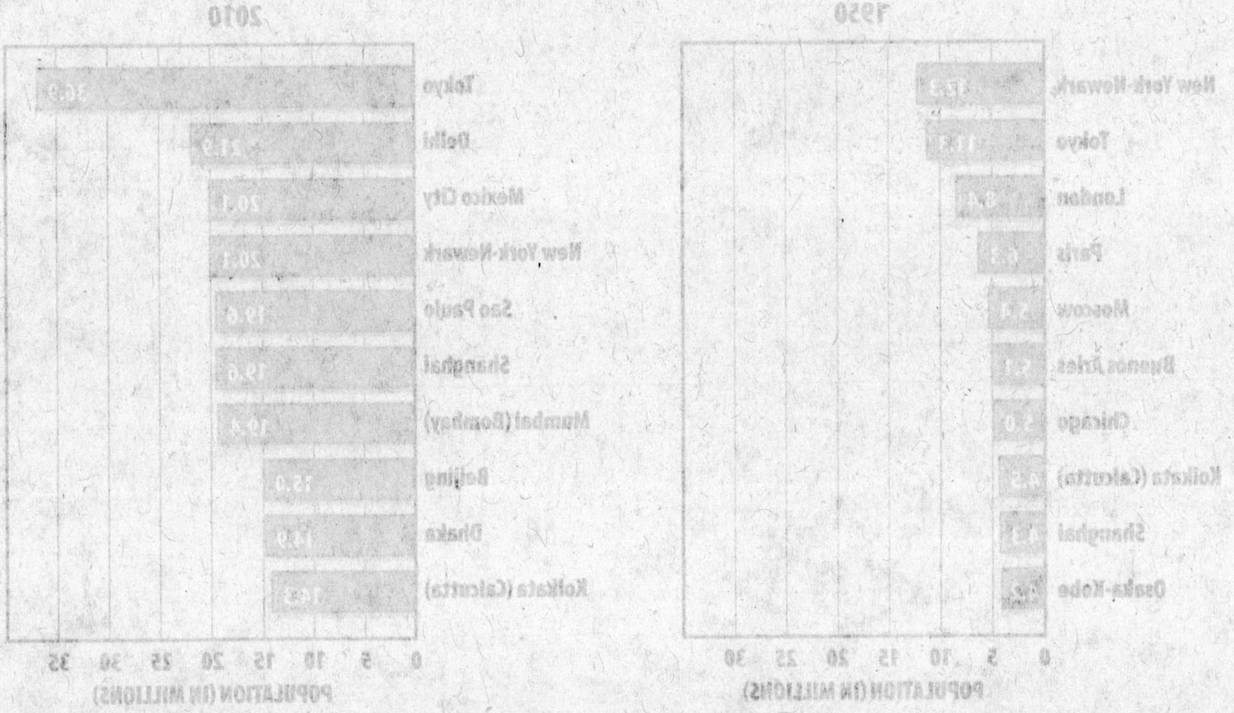

NAME ____________________ DATE ____________ CLASS ________

Lesson Quiz 16-1

networks

Social Change and Collective Behavior

DIRECTIONS: Completion Write the word or phrase that correctly completes each statement.

1. For sociologists, social change occurs when many members of the society adopt new ____________.

2. Alexis de Tocqueville made a key assumption in predicting social change in the United States when he stated that human nature would ____________.

3. A series of steps that lead gradually to a result is called a ____________.

4. Sociologists who study the growth, size, composition, distribution, and movement of human populations are ____________.

5. The sudden and complete overthrow of an existing social or political order is a ____________.

DIRECTIONS: Multiple Choice Indicate the answer choice that best completes the statement or answers the question.

______ 6. Compared to the long history of planet Earth, human social changes can best be stated as occurring
- **A.** only since the year 1.
- **B.** slowly over billions of years.
- **C.** within the past three thousand years.
- **D.** very rapidly.

______ 7. The work of Galileo and Copernicus led to the abandonment of the long-help belief that Earth was the center of the solar system. This work was an example of the social process identified as
- **A.** discovery.
- **B.** invention.
- **C.** technology.
- **D.** natural environment.

______ 8. The sociological process by which one culture or society borrows from another culture or society is
- **A.** tension.
- **B.** diffusion.
- **C.** variation.
- **D.** population.

______ 9. Sociologist Charles Tilly stated that a revolution results in the replacement of one set of
- **A.** power holders by other power holders.
- **B.** weak legislators by other legislators.
- **C.** protesting citizens by another group of protesters.
- **D.** defending soldiers by another set of defending soldiers.

______ 10. Increased global markets and new markets have made products more available to more people around the world. This statement best illustrates
- **A.** politics as a force in globalization.
- **B.** sociology as a force in globalization.
- **C.** history as a force in globalization.
- **D.** economics as a force in globalization.

NAME ____________________ DATE ____________ CLASS ____________

Lesson Quiz 16-2

networks

Social Change and Collective Behavior

DIRECTIONS: Modified True/False In the blank, indicate whether the statement is true (T) or false (F). If false, edit the statement to make it a true statement.

________ **1.** Change is one of the most variable features of American society.

________ **2.** Functionalism draws the conclusion that enactment of civil rights laws in the 1960s was a result of the struggle related to racial equality.

____

________ **3.** Equilibrium is a state of functioning and balance maintained by a society's tendency to make small adjustments to respond to change.

____

________ **4.** Many of the basic assumptions of the conflict perspective come from the writings of Karl Marx regarding social class conflicts.

____

________ **5.** Conflict theory identifies decreasing shared values as a source of social insecurity.

____

DIRECTIONS: Multiple Choice Indicate the answer choice that best completes the statement or answers the question.

________ **6.** The functionalist perspective states that a society in the process of change will

A. remain at stability.

B. move from stability to temporary instability and back to stability.

C. begin and rest at instability.

D. move from instability to temporary instability, where it will remain.

________ **7.** The focus of conflict theorists as it relates to social change is on

A. urbanism.

B. equilibrium.

C. interest groups.

D. dynamic proportions.

________ **8.** Based on symbolic interactionism, the nature and frequency of social interactions are affected by the extent to which people share

A. meanings.

B. family members.

C. economy.

D. transitional development.

________ **9.** Which historical figure's views focused on the conflict between two opposing social classes?

A. Ralf Dahrendorf

B. William Ogburn

C. Talcott Parsons

D. Karl Marx

________ **10.** Sociologist Ferdinand Tönnies stated that social interaction prior to the Industrial Revolution was based on

A. cost burdens.

B. shared tradition.

C. change response.

D. polarizing factions.

NAME ______________________ DATE ______________ CLASS __________

Lesson Quiz 16-3

networks

Social Change and Collective Behavior

DIRECTIONS: Modified True/False In the blank, indicate whether the statement is true (T) or false (F). If false, edit the statement to make it a true statement.

______ **1.** Collective behavior describes how people behave when they are united by a single short-term goal.

____

______ **2.** Fashion is a way of dressing or behaving that is widely accepted and rarely changes.

____

______ **3.** Planking and streaking are examples of rumors.

____

______ **4.** Contagion theory focuses on the spread of serious illness in a crowd.

____

______ **5.** Behavior among members of dispersed collectivities is not highly individualized.

____

DIRECTIONS: Multiple Choice Indicate the answer choice that best completes the statement or answers the question.

______ **6.** The type of crowd that has a specific purpose and follows accepted norms for appropriate behavior is identified by sociologists as

A. casual.
B. restrictive.
C. expressive.
D. conventional.

______ **7.** Which is based on false beliefs?

A. panic
B. aggregate
C. mass hysteria
D. convergence theory

______ **8.** An urban legend is most like a(n)

A. fairy tale.
B. historical romance.
C. science magazine article.
D. moralistic tale.

______ **9.** An episode of largely random destruction and violence carried out by a crowd is a

A. riot.
B. fad.
C. mob.
D. rumor.

______ **10.** Emergent-norm theory stresses the similarity between crowd behavior and

A. daily social action.
B. intentional congregation.
C. shared community values.
D. frequent mood transmission.

NAME ______________________ DATE ______________ CLASS __________

Lesson Quiz 16-4

networks

Social Change and Collective Behavior

DIRECTIONS: Completion Write the word or phrase that correctly completes each statement.

1. The theory that holds that certain conditions must exist for social movements to occur is the ______________.

2. The theory that contends that social movements compete with one another for resources is the ______________.

3. In society, there is no stimulus for change without some form of ______________.

4. The factor that must occur to galvanize people into action is called a ______________.

5. The four basic types of social movements are redemptive, reformative, revolutionary, and ______________.

DIRECTIONS: Multiple Choice Indicate the answer choice that best completes the statement or answers the question.

_____ **6.** Most social movements set out to stimulate

A. change.
B. resources.
C. leadership.
D. movement.

_____ **7.** Which person was a leader of a suffrage movement?

A. Martin Luther King, Jr.
B. Mohandas Gandhi
C. Susan B. Anthony
D. David Aberle

_____ **8.** A reformative movement attempts to effect

A. total change in society.
B. radical change within individuals.
C. limited change in society.
D. minor change within individuals.

_____ **9.** A social movement is the most highly structured, rational, and enduring type of

A. function and form.
B. collective behavior.
C. effective government.
D. ambiguity and analysis.

_____ **10.** When Mao Zedong led a movement in China, it resulted in

A. substantial income for the Chinese.
B. minor changes in Chinese society.
C. additional civil rights for the Chinese.
D. radical transformation of Chinese society.

NAME ______________________ DATE ______________ CLASS __________

Chapter 16 Test, Form A

networks

Social Change and Collective Behavior

DIRECTIONS: Matching Match each item with the correct statement below.

_______ **1.** rumor

_______ **2.** value-added theory

_______ **3.** invention

_______ **4.** resource-mobilization theory

_______ **5.** social processes

_______ **6.** mass hysteria

_______ **7.** war

_______ **8.** fad

_______ **9.** urbanism

_______ **10.** instability

A. distinctive way of life shared by people living in a city

B. collective anxiety created by acceptance of one or more false beliefs

C. series of steps leading to change on a societal level

D. a fashion, mannerism, or activity that spreads rapidly and disappears quickly

E. creation of something new from previously existing items or processes

F. lack of permanence

G. organized, armed conflict that occurs within a society or between nations

H. widely circulating piece of information that is not verified as being true or false

I. idea holding that certain conditions must exist for social movements to occur

J. focuses on the process through which members of a social movement secure and use the materials needed to advance their cause

DIRECTIONS: Multiple Choice Indicate the answer choice that best completes the statement or answers the question.

_______ **11.** Which statement accurately states one of Alexis de Tocqueville's key assumptions during the early 1800s in predicting social change in the United States?

A. Change is affected by the past and history strictly dictates the future.

B. The availability of material resources (such as land, minerals, and rich soils) limits and directs social change.

C. Equality will denigrate the trend toward centralized government.

D. Major social institutions (such as the family, religion, and the state) will cease to exist.

_______ **12.** Humans first learned that fire could be used for cooking, and they later learned it could be used to clear fields and to create ash for fertilizers. All of these examples can be sociologically identified as

A. inventions.

B. diffusion.

C. incentive.

D. discoveries.

_______ **13.** Sociologists state that, in most cases, the new social order created by a successful revolution is likely to be a(n)

A. completely new structure.

B. compromise between the old and the new.

C. unstable government whose duration is short.

D. uncivilized group of militants acting on behalf of few viewpoints.

_______ **14.** The theories of social stability formulated by functionalist sociologists William Ogburn and Talcott Parsons can best be describes as focusing on

A. economy. **C.** equilibrium.

B. proportion. **D.** opportunity.

_______ **15.** Sociologist Ferdinand Tönnies stated that interaction in urban society tends to be impersonal because

A. we frequently do not know the people with whom we interact.

B. we are fighting with one another over limited resources.

C. everyone is in such a hurry.

D. people in a city can interact only in crowds.

_______ **16.** Suppose there has just been an auto accident on a city street. Many neighbors have come out of their homes to stand on the sidewalk and chat as they watch the police and ambulance workers handle the accident scene. The neighbors' action can best be identified as

A. fad. **C.** rumor.

B. mass hysteria. **D.** collective behavior.

_______ **17.** Which statement regarding fashion is most accurate?

A. It is generally avoided by mass media. **C.** It fails to relate to politics.

B. It is rarely widely accepted. **D.** It continually changes.

_______ **18.** Alligators living in the sewers of large cities, huge gangs attacking people in malls, and a man waking up in a hotel room to discover his kidney has been stolen by organ thieves provide good examples of

A. riot. **C.** panic.

B. urban legends. **D.** spontaneous actions.

_______ **19.** Which is a fundamentally important characteristic of a social movement?

A. small number of people

B. diverse goals among members

C. structured organization

D. activity sustained through a short time period

_______ **20.** A crowd that is ready to use violence to achieve a purpose can most accurately be sociologically identified as a(n)

A. aggregate.
B. threat.
C. riot.
D. mob.

DIRECTIONS: Essays Answer the following questions on a separate sheet of paper.

21. Distinguish among contagion theory, emergent-norm theory, and convergence theory. Provide an example that is relevant to each. Explain which theory you would most like to research if you were a sociologist.

22. Identify and distinguish among four primary types of social movements and provide an example of each. Select one of these movements you would like to begin in the United States or elsewhere in the world. Explain why you would like to begin this movement—and whether it would likely be successful.

" An example of [the value-added] process is the conversion of iron ore into finished automobiles by a number of stages of processing. Relevant stages would be mining, smelting, tempering, shaping, and combining the steel with other parts, painting, delivering to retailer, and selling. Each stage 'adds its value' to the final cost of the finished product. The key element in this example is that the earlier stages must combine according to a certain pattern before the next stage can contribute its particular value to the finished product. . . . "

—Neil J. Smelser, from *Theory of Collective Behavior*, 2011

23. How does the quote illustrate the value-added theory of social movements? Explain whether you think it would be effective to add or delete conditions to explain social movements.

NAME ______________________ DATE ______________ CLASS ____________

Chapter 16 Test, Form B

networks

Social Change and Collective Behavior

DIRECTIONS: Matching Match each item with the correct statement below.

______ **1.** revolution

______ **2.** collective behavior

______ **3.** equilibrium

______ **4.** dynamic

______ **5.** fashion

______ **6.** diffusion

______ **7.** social movement

______ **8.** discovery

______ **9.** convergence theory

______ **10.** urban legend

A. process by which one culture or society borrows from another

B. marked by continuous and productive activity or change

C. moralistic tale passed along by friends and acquaintances that focuses on current concerns and fears

D. sudden and complete overthrow of a social or political order

E. most highly structured, rational, and enduring form of group behavior

F. widely accepted pattern of action that changes periodically

G. idea that crowds are formed by people who deliberately congregate with like-minded others

H. state of functioning and balance maintained by a society's tendency to make small adjustments to change

I. process by which something is learned or reinterpreted

J. spontaneous action of people who are responding to similar stimuli

DIRECTIONS: Multiple Choice Indicate the answer choice that best completes the statement or answers the question.

______ **11.** Which statement accurately reflects the forms of government in the United States and Britain?

A. Both have developed into democracies.

B. Both have developed from a royal past.

C. Both have developed from concepts of colonialism.

D. Both have developed into governmental forms in the same way.

______ **12.** Which statement best describes Alexis de Tocqueville's statements during the early 1830s regarding American society?

A. Overall, the statements were remarkably accurate.

B. Overall, the statements focused on the pace of change.

C. Overall, the statements directed readers to European history.

D. Overall, the statements seemed more appropriate for French society.

______ **13.** The Arab Spring, which occurred in the Middle East and North Africa in 2011, is an example of

A. variation.

B. diffusion.

C. revolution.

D. conversion.

Chapter 16 Test, Form B *cont.*

Social Change and Collective Behavior

_______ **14.** Ferdinand Tönnies stated that social interaction in urban society was

A. revolutionary and reoriented.

B. impersonal and fragmented.

C. polarizing and competitive.

D. industrial and selective.

_______ **15.** According to conflict perspective, social change is the result of

A. reliance on small adjustments.

B. continuity in specific political settings.

C. struggles for scarce resources.

D. decreases in the quantity of shared meanings.

_______ **16.** During 1999, many newspaper, television, and magazine journalists circulated stories of questionable truth, stating that computer glitches could cause catastrophic events at the stroke of midnight on the last day of the year. Sociologically, the journalists' statements can best be identified as

A. collective behavior.

B. rumors.

C. fads.

D. insecure individualization.

_______ **17.** Which theories related to crowd control assume that individuals are merely responding to people around them?

A. convergence and contagion

B. contagion and emergent-norm

C. emergent-norm and convergence

D. convergence, emergent-norm, and contagion

_______ **18.** The type of crowd formed by people who are taking an airplane flight or watching a film can be most accurately sociologically identified as a(an)

A. casual crowd.

B. expressive crowd.

C. momentary crowd.

D. conventional crowd.

_______ **19.** Which factor influencing social change is most exemplified by changing demographics?

A. population

B. technology

C. revolution and war

D. natural environment

_______ **20.** An organized, armed conflict that occurs within a society or between nations can most accurately and specifically be identified as a

A. riot.

B. variation.

C. war.

D. demographic.

DIRECTIONS: Essay Answer the following questions on a separate sheet of paper.

21. Compare and contrast the value-added theory and the resource-mobilization theory of social movements. Provide examples of each, and explain which theory you believe will be more relevant during the next five years.

22. Define and discuss globalization as related to diffusion. Provide an example of the impact of globalization. Explain whether globalization has been an agent of diffusion during recent decades—and whether you think this is likely to change during upcoming decades.

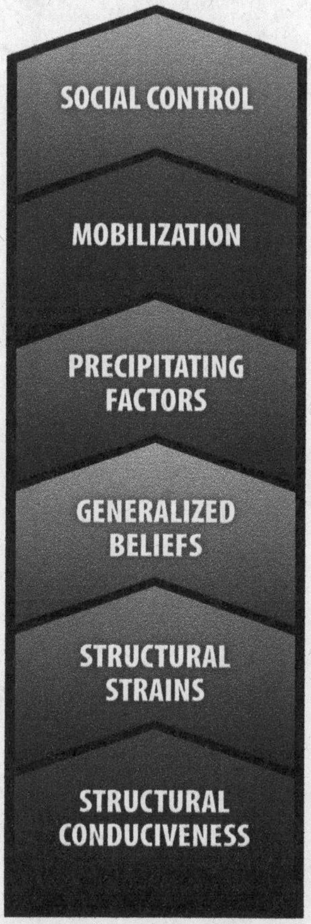

23. What theory that explains social movements does the graphic illustrate? What does the organization of the graphic show? Briefly explain how the theory explains how social movements develop?

networks

Chapter 16 Test, Form B *cont.*

Social Change and Collective Behavior

CHAPTER 1

LESSON QUIZ 1-1

True/False

1. True
2. False
3. False
4. False
5. True

Multiple Choice

6. C 7. A 8. B 9. D 10. C

LESSON QUIZ 1-2

Matching

1. D 2. C 3. E 4. A 5. B

Multiple Choice

6. D 7. A 8. D 9. B 10. D

LESSON QUIZ 1-3

Modified True/False

1. False—A manifest function is INTENDED AND RECOGNIZED.
2. True
3. True
4. False—Social structure refers to the RECURRING patterns of social behaviors in a group or society.
5. False—Functionalism assumes that societies WILL return to a state of stability after periods of upheaval.

Multiple Choice

6. D 7. C 8. C 9. A 10. A

CHAPTER 1 TEST, FORM A

Matching

1. D 2. B 3. E 4. C 5. A
6. H 7. I 8. J 9. F 10. G

Multiple Choice

11. B 12. C 13. D 14. B 15. D
16. A 17. C 18. A 19. C 20. A

Essays

21. Answers will vary but may include any of the following reasons.
By studying sociology we may: know more about patterns of behavior shared by members of a group or society; we may be able to explain events—e.g., divorce, suicide, delinquency; we may learn more about: categories of people, social structure, conformity, behavior. Studying sociology helps us to foster positive interaction and facilitate better communication with others; this study helps us to not be prisoners of social forces that affect our lives; other schools have established such a program and have been highly successful and recognized for their efforts.

22. This quote is still relevant today. The effects of poverty are felt most strongly by an individual who must make difficult economic choices to survive. However, the government makes plans to deal with "group" poverty. The most effective programs deal with large groups of people. This quote also provides a real-world illustration of one of the important differences in the way psychologists and sociologists study human behavior. In this instance, a psychologist might study the effects of being poor on a poor person. A sociologist would study the effects of poverty on a group of people.

CHAPTER 1 TEST, FORM B

Matching

1. E 2. D 3. H 4. A 5. C
6. G 7. F 8. I 9. B 10. J

Multiple Choice

11. D 12. B 13. C 14. C 15. B
16. A 17. D 18. C 19. D 20. B

Essays

21. Jane Addams suggests that the immigrants will become assimilated in the American culture. The settlement will expose them to new customs and help them to learn English. She believed that a settlement house was a force for social good. In the past, people who came to this country were anxious to be thought of as assimilated. They wanted to be treated like other Americans who came before them. Today, we prize the diversity that different groups of people bring to this country. For example, think of all the different customs and kinds of foods

you can find in the many diverse restaurants present in an American city. In many American cities, ethnic-based parades are often seen on a yearly basis. People are happy to celebrate their national customs even as they enjoy the freedoms living in the United States brings them.

22. Student answers will vary. Possible answers may include:

Universities: The University of Chicago established the first sociology department.

Other schools following suit: Harvard, Columbia, Stanford, University of California at Berkeley, etc. Individuals: C. Wright Mills—sociological imagination, relationship evident between personal lives and events within society; Jane Addams—social justice/exploitation of lower class, founder of Hull House in Chicago, peace movement, women's suffrage; W.E.B. Du Bois—Pan-African movement, teacher, social activist, "Negro problem."

23. Student answers will vary. Arranging the five key concepts in a circle implies equality—no concept is more important than any other. When it is used, a circular arrangement of materials in an illustration hints that there is no beginning and no end. A straight-line arrangement implies the passage of time or a stepped-out process, one stage following another from beginning to an end. If these five key concepts were arranged as a pyramid, it would hint at a hierarchy with the most important concept at the top supported by lesser topics.

CHAPTER 2

LESSON QUIZ 2-1

Matching

1. D **2.** C **3.** A **4.** E **5.** B

Multiple Choice

6. D **7.** B **8.** C **9.** D **10.** A

LESSON QUIZ 2-2

True/False

1. True
2. False
3. True
4. False
5. True

Multiple Choice

6. B **7.** C **8.** C **9.** D **10.** B

LESSON QUIZ 2-3

True/False

1. True
2. False
3. True
4. False
5. True

Multiple Choice

6. C **7.** B **8.** D **9.** A **10.** D

CHAPTER 2 TEST, FORM A

Matching

1. D **2.** A **3.** B **4.** F **5.** E
6. I **7.** J **8.** C **9.** G **10.** H

Multiple Choice

11. A **12.** D **13.** B **14.** D **15.** A
16. D **17.** C **18.** C **19.** D **20.** D

Essays

21. Answers should mention three of the following: sensitivity; confidentiality; objectivity; verifiability; truthful reporting; respecting the dignity, integrity, and privacy of research subjects; balance includes consideration of the participant in relation to the importance of the data collected; finally there is no possibility that anyone could be hurt or defamed due to the research process.

22. The graph with the line that moves up toward the right would show a direct correlation between the amount of time studied and a good grade in class. The line would first go up toward the right for a time and then would head downward toward the right beginning at the point the data showed the negative correlation between time studied and the grade received.

CHAPTER 2 TEST, FORM B

Matching

1. F **2.** B **3.** E **4.** C **5.** D
6. J **7.** A **8.** I **9.** H **10.** G

Multiple Choice

11. B **12.** C **13.** A **14.** A **15.** B
16. A **17.** A **18.** C **19.** B **20.** C

Essays

21. To explain, predict, and control phenomena, a researcher follows a plan and procedures for collecting and analyzing data. A research plan addresses why and how the research will be conducted. Steps include, among others: isolating/selecting a topic; defining a problem/situation; deciding on the use of quantitative and qualitative data and field research (include consideration of ethical issues). Focus should be solely on data required to perform research. Finally, a good research plan indicates a solvable problem or situation to study. A good research plan can help identify a problem that cannot be studied.

22. Students should point out that respect for others is a defining characteristic of the field of sociology. Sociologists endeavor to meet this standard in a number of ways, including following the Code of Ethics, adhering to professional standards for methods and objectivity, endeavoring to report findings truthfully, and protecting the privacy of research subjects.

CHAPTER 3

LESSON QUIZ 3-1

True/False

1. False
2. True
3. True
4. False
5. True

Multiple Choice

6. B **7.** B **8.** D **9.** C **10.** B

LESSON QUIZ 3-2

True/False

1. True
2. False
3. False
4. True
5. True

Multiple Choice

6. A **7.** C **8.** B **9.** C **10.** B

LESSON QUIZ 3-3

Matching

1. D **2.** B **3.** E **4.** A **5.** C

Multiple Choice

6. C **7.** A **8.** B **9.** C **10.** C

LESSON QUIZ 3-4

True/False

1. False
2. True
3. True
4. False
5. True

Multiple Choice

6. A **7.** C **8.** A **9.** A **10.** B

LESSON QUIZ 3-5

Matching

1. B **2.** D **3.** E **4.** C **5.** B

Multiple Choice

6. C **7.** B **8.** A **9.** D **10.** A

CHAPTER 3 TEST, FORM A

Matching

1. B **2.** E **3.** A **4.** D **5.** J
6. G **7.** H **8.** C **9.** I **10.** F

Multiple Choice

11. A **12.** A **13.** C **14.** A **15.** B
16. C **17.** C **18.** A **19.** C **20.** D

Essays

21. Student should refer to the Sapir-Whorf theory of language development. They should discuss how language shapes thought and by extension, action.

22. Some key words/phrases to look for in answers include: diversity or similarity; concept of democracy; equality; enculturation—learning the traditional content of a culture and assimilating its practices and values; socialization—learning the social norms; social justice; assist students in realizing similarities of all people; all people have value; sharing of technology; improve relationships; free expression of talents and abilities; human relations.

23. Answers may vary. Adolescents are usually concerned about control issues. Many adolescents think that they are able to make their own decisions. Parents are concerned about the welfare of their children. They are concerned about safety issues and of helping their children develop ways of making wise decisions. Thus, adolescence can be a difficult period of conflict between parents and children. Parents should remember that adolescence is a period of "trial" for both parties. Seeing their parent's point of view and accepting that they might not like all of the decisions their parents make should help adolescents understand that parents usually have the future welfare of their children in mind. This is a normal period of conflict that all people pass through—some more successfully than others.

CHAPTER 3 TEST, FORM B

Matching

1. J **2.** B **3.** A **4.** E **5.** D
6. I **7.** H **8.** G **9.** C **10.** F

Multiple Choice

11. C **12.** A **13.** C **14.** A **15.** C
16. D **17.** C **18.** C **19.** C **20.** A

Essays

21. Folkways are not considered vital to group welfare; those who violate them are not considered deviant; reactions vary according to situation and location; possibly unconsciously created; folkways may become mores or laws. Mores concern conduct related to right and wrong and the well-being of society; violation of conformity brings extreme social disapproval; taboos– violation demands punishment; unconsciously created; may be somewhat deviant; important source for laws; but not all taboos become laws. Laws constitute a formal norm enforced by officials; consciously created and enforced; deviant behavior; last chance when folkways and mores fail. Formal and informal sanctions may result from violating any of the three norms.

22. Answers may vary. Students should demonstrate an understanding of the process by which cultural values migrate from one cultural context to another. Clothing styles, movies, entertainment forms, and different sports have also shown cross-cultural diffusion.

23. Answers will vary depending on the country selected. For example, Americans usually do not remove their shoes when visiting someone's home. Most Americans do bring a gift to a dinner or party held in someone's home. Most of the items listed involve greetings or expressions of hospitality. Customs and norms usually develop over time. The reasons for many of these norms and customs are probably not even remembered. Many may involve religious beliefs. For example, norms and customs involving deceased people are often very strict—even to the selection of flower color in some cultures.

CHAPTER 4

LESSON QUIZ 4-1

True/False

1. False
2. True
3. False
4. True
5. True

Multiple Choice

6. D **7.** C **8.** C **9.** A **10.** C

LESSON QUIZ 4-2

Matching

1. D **2.** A **3.** C **4.** E **5.** B

Multiple Choice

6. A **7.** A **8.** D **9.** B **10.** D

LESSON QUIZ 4-3

True/False

1. True
2. True
3. False
4. True
5. False

Multiple Choice

6. D **7.** A **8.** C **9.** C **10.** D

LESSON QUIZ 4-4

Matching

1. C **2.** E **3.** D **4.** B **5.** A

Multiple Choice

6. D **7.** D **8.** B **9.** D **10.** B

LESSON QUIZ 4-5

Modified True/False

1. False— A public university is NOT an example of a total institution.
2. True
3. True
4. False— People OFTEN use peer groups as a tool for anticipatory socialization.
5. False— Anticipatory socialization RARELY occurs in prisons and other total institutions.

Multiple Choice

6. C **7.** C **8.** D **9.** A **10.** C

CHAPTER 4 TEST, FORM A

Matching

1. H **2.** A **3.** B **4.** E **5.** D
6. F **7.** I **8.** G **9.** J **10.** C

Multiple Choice

11. D **12.** D **13.** C **14.** A **15.** B
16. B **17.** B **18.** B **19.** D **20.** B

Essays

21. Socialization is the cultural process of learning how to participate in group life. Socialization begins at birth and continues throughout life. If a person is properly socialized, that person can fit into all kinds of social groups. Socialization is critically important for society to help people adjust to new situations throughout life.

Socialization helps maintain social institutions. Children learn the basic norms, beliefs, and values of our society from parents and school. If this were not the case, society as we know it could not exist. It would be fragmented and chaotic.

22. Schools are major agents of socialization. For the first time, many of the child's relationships with other people are impersonal. Rewards and punishments are based on performance rather than affection. The socialization process in school is based on the hidden curriculum, the informal and unofficial aspects of culture that children are taught in preparation for life. The hidden curriculum teaches children discipline, order, cooperation, and conformity. These characteristics are required for success in the adult world of work. Schools have rules and regulations to cover most activities–how to dress, how to wear one's hair, and when to speak in class. Teachers reward children with praise and acceptance when they behave properly and exhibit desirable attitudes.

23. Charisse wants more freedom to have boyfriends. She wants to make her own decisions. Charisse's father is probably concerned about his daughter's safety. His attitudes show protective behaviors toward her. He may not be entirely convinced that his daughter is capable of making wise decisions about her choice of boyfriends. These kinds of disagreements are typical of parents and teenagers when young people begin to exhibit independent behavior.

CHAPTER 4 TEST, FORM B

Matching

1. B **2.** J **3.** A **4.** C **5.** E
6. H **7.** F **8.** G **9.** D **10.** I

Multiple Choice

11. D **12.** B **13.** B **14.** A **15.** B
16. C **17.** C **18.** B **19.** A **20.** A

Essays

21. Printed media, such as magazines, books, and newspapers are not included in the time line shown in the diagram. Print media predates the other forms of media shown. They may have not been included because they are not the most important sources of information for most people in our technological age. People are now used to having almost instantaneous sources of information. Printed media takes time to print and deliver to consumers. However, they are still relevant today as sources of information and analysis. Printed media can offer the perspective of the time it takes to analyze a situation and present it to readers.

22. Mead viewed significant others as an important part of the socialization process because these are the people whose judgments we most respect. Some significant others remain constant throughout a person's life—family members, for example. While some significant others change, a spouse for example. Significant others often serve as role models.

CHAPTER 5

LESSON QUIZ 5-1

Modified True/False

1. True
2. False—Deciding to get married is NOT an example of an ascribed status.
3. False—A status set might include being a college graduate AND being an American citizen.
4. True
5. True

Multiple Choice

6. D	**7.** B	**8.** C	**9.** A	**10.** C

LESSON QUIZ 5-2

Modified True/False

1. True
2. False—Young people occupy MANY status positions in society and LIKE ADULTS they ALSO EXPERIENCE role strain.
3. True
4. False—Social interaction INVOLVES ANY OF THE moments of interaction among people.
3. True

Multiple Choice

6. A	**7.** D	**8.** A	**9.** C	**10.** C

LESSON QUIZ 5-3

Matching

1. B	**2.** E	**3.** A	**4.** C	**5.** D

Multiple Choice

6. B	**7.** B	**8.** A	**9.** B	**10.** C

LESSON QUIZ 5-4

True/False

1. True
2. True
3. False
4. False
5. True

Multiple Choice

6. A	**7.** B	**8.** B	**9.** D	**10.** B

CHAPTER 5 TEST, FORM A

Matching

1. J	**2.** G	**3.** B	**4.** E	**5.** C
6. H	**7.** I	**8.** F	**9.** D	**10.** A

Multiple Choice

11. C	**12.** C	**13.** B	**14.** B	**15.** A
16. D	**17.** D	**18.** C	**19.** A	**20.** B

Essays

21. A variety of people are needed to fulfill society's needs such as barbers, bankers, service suppliers, teachers, and cooks. Members of modern industrial society are interdependent. In a postindustrial society, there is a creation of new social norms. Characteristics of industrial societies are: manufacturing industry; the production of tangible goods; blue-collar workers; machinery and assembly lines; technology that is implemented without testing its effects on the environment; hand-drawn graphic arts; increased social instability; increasing crime rate. Characteristics of postindustrial societies are: service and information industries; provision of intangible services such as health, recreation, and government; white collar workers; technical knowledge; technological change that is planned and assessed in advance; reliance on computer modeling; decreased social instability; decreasing crime rate.

22. Rights are behaviors individuals expect from others. Examples: a person makes a confession knowing his priest has vowed to keep the confession confidential; a patient has a right to expect that her physician will keep anything discussed in confidence. Some rights are codified into laws—the confidentiality of medical records is an example. Students have a right to learn in a school or home environment. Obligations are behaviors that individuals are expected to perform toward others. Examples: a Catholic priest must keep all confessions confidential; a lawyer has a duty to assist a client with a legal problem to the best of her or his ability. A teacher has an obligation to teach students by creating a positive learning environment. Students have an obligation to attend class and complete assignments, and treat their teachers and other school staff with respect.

23. The experiment lasted for a week. In this time, the volunteers quickly assumed their assigned status. One reason why this might have happened is because this investigation took place in a tightly-controlled environment. There was little room for any individual to make a choice that might have limited their trauma or increased their use of power. The prisoners were powerless, the guards held all the power. The investigators ignored personality traits in making their decision. They assigned the roles people played by a coin flip. The investigation was ended quickly because the data showed that the prisoners were emotionally suffering from the treatment of the guards.

CHAPTER 5 TEST, FORM B

Matching

1. F	**2.** J	**3.** B	**4.** C	**5.** A
6. H	**7.** I	**8.** G	**9.** D	**10.** E

Multiple Choice

11. A	**12.** C	**13.** B	**14.** D	**15.** A
16. B	**17.** D	**18.** D	**19.** C	**20.** A

Essays

21. A status is the position a person occupies within a social structure. It can be ascribed or assigned at birth (example: princess or prince, heiress, or upper class) or achieved, earned, or chosen (example: president, gang leader). Roles describe performance or conduct in carrying out interactions (example: labor negotiator or secretary of state). A person occupies more than one status at a time—this is a status set (example: middle class, employed male, father, husband, son, and PTA president). Social structure is a learned veritable "social map" we use in various group situations that spare us confusion. Examples: When going to a prom or formal event a student wouldn't wear jeans and tennis shoes; eating fried chicken with fingers may be appropriate at home but isn't always appropriate in a formal setting.

22. Japan and the United States invest a great deal of money in research and development. In addition they have manufacturing industries capable of producing high-technology goods that can be exported. In all probability China does not invest as much in research and development as Japan and the United States. But their large working population and tremendous production capacity can manufacture huge amounts of technology goods that can be exported.

CHAPTER 6

LESSON QUIZ 6-1

Modified True/False

1. True
2. False—The members of a social CATEGORY all have similar social CHARACTERISTICS.
3. True
4. True
5. False—Primary relationships develop more easily in PRIMARY GROUPS.

Multiple Choice

6. C	**7.** D	**8.** C	**9.** C	**10.** A

LESSON QUIZ 6-2

Modified True/False

1. True
2. False—In order to use a reference group to evaluate yourself, you DO NOT need to be a member of that group.
3. True
4. False—One characteristic of a social network is that it LACKS clear group boundaries.
5. True

Multiple Choice

6. C	**7.** A	**8.** B	**9.** A	**10.** B

LESSON QUIZ 6-3

Matching

1. A	**2.** C	**3.** E	**4.** B	**5.** D

Multiple Choice

6. B	**7.** A	**8.** A	**9.** A	**10.** D

LESSON QUIZ 6-4

True/False

1. True
2. False
3. True
4. False
5. True

Multiple Choice

6. A **7.** C **8.** B **9.** C **10.** D

CHAPTER 6 TEST, FORM A

Matching

1. G **2.** C **3.** E **4.** B **5.** A
6. I **7.** D **8.** H **9.** F **10.** J

Multiple Choice

11. B **12.** D **13.** D **14.** C **15.** D
16. A **17.** B **18.** A **19.** C **20.** C

Essay

21. Weber was the first to analyze the nature of bureaucracy and he feared the dehumanizing effects. In preindustrial societies, decision makers were chosen on the basis of family or wealth. As societies became industrialized, Weber recognized that bureaucracies were technically superior to any other form of organization. In industrial societies, rationalization, or a mind-set that emphasizes knowledge, reason, and planning, was on the rise. A new kind of organization was required and bureaucracies had the advantages needed.

22. Student answers will vary but may include the following examples. High school—goals are to prepare students for future work force; teach basics of reading, writing, and math; socialization. Corporations—goals are profits, stability, and advanced style of living.

23. Student answers will vary but may include the following explanations. People may be willing to follow an authority figure against their better judgment because they assume the person in authority knows what she is doing and has asked them to do something that follows sound logic and reason. People are taught to respect and obey authority figures such as parents, teachers, police officers, and government officials from a young age, and the idea that we should conform to authority is reinforced through many aspects of society. People are often worried about the repercussions of not obeying an authority figure and are often eager to please those who are in charge. Accept all reasonable answers.

CHAPTER 6 TEST, FORM B

Matching

1. B **2.** A **3.** D **4.** E **5.** C
6. J **7.** I **8.** H **9.** F **10.** G

Multiple Choice

11. A **12.** B **13.** A **14.** B **15.** D
16. A **17.** B **18.** C **19.** B **20.** D

Essay

21. Primary groups are characterized by members who are emotionally close, know each other well, and seek out each other's company. These groups provide the following functions: emotional support, socialization, and conformity. Examples: family and/or relatives, close friends/best friends, neighbors, and religious communities. These groups emphasize the "we" feeling. They are intimate, personal, caring, and fulfilling.

Secondary groups are impersonal, goal-oriented, and designed for a specific purpose. They emphasize the "us" feeling. These groups don't comprise a significant part of one's life. They dissolve when the goal is met. Examples: corporations, clerk and customer, dentist and patient, school counselor and student, bureaucracy, and U.S. military.

22. Membership in educational organizations increases to the mid 40s, and then begins to decline. Membership in religious organizations is weakest in the youngest age group represented and increases across all age groups. One explanation can be that people stop belonging to educational groups when their schooling stops and their career paths are set. Religion seems to be less important or relevant to the lives of most young people, however this trend reverses as people age.

CHAPTER 7

LESSON QUIZ 7-1

True/False

1. True
2. True
3. True
4. False
5. False

Multiple Choice

6. B 7. A 8. B 9. A 10. B

LESSON QUIZ 7-2

Modified True/False

1. False—Deviance CAN ALSO affect society in POSITIVE ways.
2. True
3. True
4. False— According to control theory, deviance is the consequence of too FEW social bonds.
5. True

Multiple Choice

6. C 7. B 8. C 9. D 10. B

LESSON QUIZ 7-3

Matching

1. C 2. E 3. A 4. D 5. B

Multiple Choice

6. C 7. C 8. A 9. C 10. B

LESSON QUIZ 7-4

Modified True/False

1. True
2. True
3. False—White-collar crimes are generally AS significant AS other forms of crime.
4. True
5. False—According to conflict theory, people who have less power in society are also MORE likely to be convicted of crimes.

Multiple Choice

6. D 7. A 8. C 9. A 10. D

LESSON QUIZ 7-5

Completion

1. a crime
2. decreased slightly
3. recidivism
4. rehabilitation
5. Incarceration

Multiple Choice

6. B 7. B 8. B 9. C 10. B

CHAPTER 7 TEST, FORM A

Matching

1. A 2. C 3. E 4. I 5. D
6. H 7. F 8. B 9. G 10. J

Multiple Choice

11. A 12. D 13. B 14. A 15. C
16. A 17. A 18. B 19. D 20. D

Essays

21. Deviance can clarify and adjust norms. Example: Gambling was generally illegal in early America; now several states approve and sanction it. Deviance can be a temporary safety valve (i.e., loud music, trendy clothing). This may be a rebellion against adults and authority figures. Deviance increases unity within society or a group and may strengthen its commitment to values (i.e., intervention in a child abuse act; protect the child at all costs) and promote social change (i.e., women's right to vote). Other examples: diffusion—blending norms from different cultures; chaos inhibitor—slows down or stops chaos from getting out of control.

22. Answers will vary but may include the following examples. Primary deviance: an isolated act occurs (i.e., break a neighbor's window and other kinds of property crime).

    Secondary deviance: part of one's lifestyle and personal identity (i.e., membership in a motorcycle club such as Hell's Angels, gambling, using illicit drugs, and/or white-collar crime).

23. Because deviant behavior is defined by society and is often a reflection of time and place, changes in the rate of deviant behavior can also occur. In this data, economic and social unrest may have affected youth behavior. However, the overall trend is certainly in a downward direction. Primary deviance occurs during youth does not continue into adulthood.

CHAPTER 7 TEST, FORM B

Matching

1. E 2. C 3. H 4. J 5. B
6. G 7. I 8. A 9. D 10. F

Multiple Choice

11. B 12. B 13. C 14. A 15. D
16. A 17. B 18. C 19. C 20. B

Essays

21. These answers will vary depending on students' perceptions about crime and deviance. Some students might feel that incarceration is the most effective way of dealing with criminal behavior. Certainly, when in jail, an offender will not commit a crime against people that are not in jail. Other students may feel that this is the most expensive way of dealing with offenders, and there is little evidence that incarceration lessens the rate of recidivism. Some students may feel that rehabilitation and restitution may be more effective than incarceration in preventing recidivism. Also, these two methods do not stigmatize an offender and may better enable the offender to behave according to societal norms in the future.

22. Deviant behavior is a matter of social definition. Society's ideas of deviance are relative to time, place, and social position. This study illustrates attitudes based on economic status. Bad behavior by people with high economic status is usually treated by society more leniently than bad behavior by people with lower economic status.

CHAPTER 8

LESSON QUIZ 8-1

True/False

1. False
2. True
3. True
4. False
5. True

Multiple Choice

6. A **7.** D **8.** D **9.** B **10.** A

LESSON QUIZ 8-2

Matching

1. E **2.** D **3.** C **4.** A **5.** B

Multiple Choice

6. A **7.** C **8.** D **9.** C **10.** B

LESSON QUIZ 8-3

Completion

1. classes
2. inheriting
3. intergenerational mobility
4. mobility
5. merit

Multiple Choice

6. D **7.** A **8.** B **9.** A **10.** D

LESSON QUIZ 8-4

True/False

1. True
2. False
3. True
4. False
5. True

Multiple Choice

6. B **7.** B **8.** C **9.** C **10.** A

CHAPTER 8 TEST, FORM A

Matching

1. G **2.** E **3.** H **4.** J **5.** D
6. F **7.** C **8.** B **9.** A **10.** I

Multiple Choice

11. A **12.** C **13.** B **14.** C **15.** A
16. C **17.** A **18.** B **19.** D **20.** B

Essays

21. Upward mobility is defined as occupational status or social class that moves in relation to merit and individual effort. There are many barriers today; Horatio Alger stories are myths. Many people have inadequate technological education and training to prepare them for the movement away from manual labor (blue collar) to a more service-oriented economy with its emphasis on non-mechanical and less routine jobs. Many jobs are given to people in other countries due to lower wages there and more company profit. Wages are generally not enough to meet basic needs much less move families to a higher rung. Values (Puritan work ethic) may be a hindrance, as well as inequalities (racial, ethnic, gender, and age) and lack of role models.

22. The graph compares three brackets: people in the top 1 percent, people in the top 20 percent, and people in the bottom 80 percent in the United States. Since wealth is defined as what you own one can infer that the top two brackets also have the highest income. The total does not add up to 100 percent because the wealth of people in the top 1 percent is actually counted twice. They are also counted in the top 20 percent group.

CHAPTER 8 TEST, FORM B

Matching

1. B **2.** C **3.** D **4.** H **5.** I
6. A **7.** J **8.** F **9.** E **10.** G

Multiple Choice

11. C **12.** C **13.** C **14.** D **15.** C
16. C **17.** A **18.** C **19.** D **20.** B

Essays

21. Upper class: 1% of population in America; upper-upper (aristocracy) by birth or inherited wealth (Ford, Carnegie); lower-upper is achievement-oriented, has earned income (i.e., Bill Gates, Ted Turner, Donald Trump); middle classes: 40-50% of population in America; upper-middle (14%) is active in voluntary and/or political organizations, college-educated, goal-oriented; middle-middle (30%) consists of small business owners and/or farmers, independent professionals, has high school education with some college degrees, some participate in political activities; working class: (lower-middle class, about 1/3 of population), has below-average income, unstable employment; working poor: (13%) hold low-skill jobs with lowest pay, have unsteady employment, are below poverty line in income; underclass: (12%) hold part-time jobs or are on public assistance, may be unemployed or from a family with a history of generational unemployment, lack education.

22. Today, thirty-seven million people (12.7 % of our population) are poor; annual income is less than $19,484 for a family of 4; 8.6% are white, 27% are African American, 27% are Latino. Minorities, female-headed households, disabled people, children under 18 years of age, people who live alone, and people who live with nonrelatives make up most of the poor. Why are they poor? Women generally earn less than men (80 cents to the dollar). There is a lack of affordable, good, safe childcare. Other factors: inadequate financial planning for the older population segment, inadequate job skills, unwed mothers, inadequate education, unemployment, generational poverty, lack of affordable housing, domestic violence, removed from nuclear family.

23. Marx would view this as a classic struggle between working people and the people who control capital. Marx would describe the power disparity between the two groups. Although the low-paying jobs required physical labor, it is clear from her phrase that the author believed that the employers wanted employee loyalty and to be free of being criticized by their employees.

CHAPTER 9

LESSON QUIZ 9-1

True/False

1. False
2. True
3. False
4. False
5. True

Multiple Choice

6. D **7.** B **8.** D **9.** A **10.** A

LESSON QUIZ 9-2

Matching

1. C **2.** D **3.** A **4.** B **5.** E

Multiple Choice

6. C **7.** D **8.** D **9.** D **10.** B

LESSON QUIZ 9-3

True/False

1. False
2. True
3. True
4. False
5. True

Multiple Choice

6. D **7.** D **8.** B **9.** A **10.** D

LESSON QUIZ 9-4

Completion

1. the legacy of slavery
2. institutionalized discrimination
3. Latinos
4. Native Americans
5. hidden unemployment

Multiple Choice

6. A **7.** D **8.** C **9.** A **10.** A

CHAPTER 9 TEST, FORM A

Matching

1. C **2.** H **3.** B **4.** J **5.** F
6. E **7.** D **8.** A **9.** I **10.** G

Multiple Choice

11. A **12.** C **13.** B **14.** B **15.** B
16. C **17.** B **18.** D **19.** D **20.** A

Essays

21. Answers will vary. Students may suggest that sometimes the table turns—the majority group becomes the minority group, with people of color in power, old networks diminished and new networks established, and so on.

22. Answers will vary, but should include some of the following characteristics. Prejudice: an attitude—involves generalizations based on biased or incomplete or slanted information; strong emotions such as anger, fear, hatred, and distrust; difficult to change negative attitudes; hate crimes may result. Examples: some whites may feel that minority families are predominantly dysfunctional and favor unemployment; some Latinos may feel that whites are bossy, condescending, and stingy.

Racism: a belief—involves judging people unfairly; assumes that one's own race or ethnic group is naturally superior to another (ethnocentricity); strong emotions; very difficult to change. Examples: members of the Ku Klux Klan and neo-Nazis believe in an inherent white supremacy.

Discrimination: a behavior—involves treating people unequally by denying them privileges that are available to others; two kinds: individual—one against another; and institutional—inequalities in society. Examples: a rental agency claims a vacant apartment is rented when an African American inquires, but offers the apartment to a white person later in the day.

23. Your view, or perception of yourself, is often a reflection of how others view you. In this quote, the three women were viewed in different contexts. They identified themselves as Americans when they were with Mexican-born family and friends. Members of the dominant culture viewed and stereotyped the women as foreigners. They viewed themselves as independent women in their relations with their fathers, who in traditional Mexican society are considered the head of the family. Members of the dominant culture may not share this view.

CHAPTER 9 TEST, FORM B

Matching

1. H **2.** E **3.** F **4.** I **5.** B
6. C **7.** J **8.** D **9.** A **10.** G

Multiple Choice

11. A **12.** A **13.** A **14.** A **15.** A
16. B **17.** A **18.** D **19.** D **20.** D

Essays

21. Asians and Pacific Islanders have higher family incomes than whites. One reason might be that Asians and Pacific Islanders enter more high-paying fields—professions such as physicians and engineers. Many African Americans and Latinos have lower paying jobs. This may be as a result of racism and poor educational opportunities. The overall incomes for all groups have increased over the years shown. Income for Asian and Pacific Islanders has shown the greatest increase.

22. Answers can include discussion of the distinction between *de jure* segregation and *de facto* segregation. Students might also discuss the barriers to assimilation faced by African Americans and other minority groups, and how funds to school districts are often not distributed equally. People are often grouped in certain school districts based on economic status. For example, the poor tend to live near other poor people; more well to do people tend to live near each other. Unequal government funding may thus contribute to *de facto* segregation in some school districts. Busing was one solution offered to correct access to better schools, but it caused other problems. Students who were bused often had school days that were much longer than local students.

LESSON QUIZ 10-1

Modified True/False

1. True
2. False—MORE variations exist within each sex than between the sexes.
3. True

4. False—The majority of sociologists believe that gender-related behavior is primarily SHAPED BY CULTURE AND SOCIETY.
5. False—Gender refers to an awareness of being masculine or feminine based on CULTURE.

Multiple Choice

6. B **7.** A **8.** B **9.** C **10.** B

LESSON QUIZ 10-2

Completion

1. keep their own power and advantage
2. based on sex
3. gender socialization
4. symbolic interactionists
5. necessary to future development

Multiple Choice

6. A **7.** D **8.** B **9.** B **10.** A

LESSON QUIZ 10-3

True/False

1. True
2. True
3. False
4. True
5. False

Multiple Choice

6. B **7.** B **8.** B **9.** C **10.** D

LESSON QUIZ 10-4

True/False

1. True
2. True
3. False
4. True
5. False

Multiple Choice

6. B **7.** B **8.** A **9.** B **10.** A

LESSON QUIZ 10-5

Completion

1. vote
2. diverse group
3. elderly women
4. three times as high
5. high incomes

Multiple Choice

6. D **7.** C **8.** A **9.** C **10.** D

CHAPTER 10 TEST, FORM A

Matching

1. H **2.** G **3.** E **4.** A **5.** B

6. I **7.** C **8.** F **9.** J **10.** D

Multiple Choice

11. B **12.** C **13.** A **14.** C **15.** C

16. C **17.** C **18.** D **19.** A **20.** C

Essays

21. Answers will vary depending on student perceptions. Students may cover any or all of the following. Students who choose biology may mention the following: the female brain is the emotional center; the male brain is the center of intellect and logic. Males appear to be more aggressive, hunters; females appear to be more passive, nurturers. Male bodies are stronger; female bodies are weaker (i.e., males can bench press more than females, males have more endurance in triathlons, etc.).

Students who choose socialization may mention the following: at birth a girl is assigned pink and is described as sweet, soft, and cute; at birth a boy is assigned blue and is described as handsome, tough, and bouncing. Children learn to behave as their parents expect (i.e., girls perform feminine activities such as sewing, art, cooking, and reading; boys perform masculine activities such as fighting, football, and horseback riding). Normative expectations are attached to each gender—Mother Earth and Father Time. Girls are thought to have good behavior and are more intelligent when young; boys are thought to be active (macho) and not as academically advanced when young. Terminology differs with jobs (language justifies differences and implies less proficiency for women). For example, men are chefs, flight attendants, waiters, office managers, ballet dancers; women are cooks, stewardesses, waitresses, secretaries, ballerinas. Behaviors are influenced by peer groups, family, and media. Magazine advertising depicts females as the sweet-smelling, well-dressed, and hair-perfect.

Men are portrayed as rough and tough, bearded, smelly beings.

22. In all races shown in the graph women make less money than men. Some explanations might be: gender bias shown in many different ways. For example, men are believed to need to work to support a family, while women work only to increase the family's standard of living; workplace longevity—since men have worked outside of the home for a longer time period than women, they have risen in corporate ranks to higher paying positions. The Lilly Ledbetter Fair Pay Act was signed by President Obama in 2009. Enforcing this law and enacting other wage protection laws should limit the differences in pay that men and women receive for the same job. Other answers are possible.

23. Students might point out the ways in which Americans also conceive of gender as two opposing sets of behavior, such as passivity in women and aggression in men. Social structure and long-held beliefs about appropriate gender roles are still prevalent in today's industrial societies. Other answers are possible.

CHAPTER 10 TEST, FORM B

Matching

1. H	**2.** D	**3.** C	**4.** J	**5.** E
6. B	**7.** F	**8.** A	**9.** I	**10.** G

Multiple Choice

11. C	**12.** A	**13.** C	**14.** B	**15.** A
16. D	**17.** A	**18.** A	**19.** B	**20.** A

Essays

21. Ageism is a set of beliefs, attitudes, norms, and values used to justify prejudice and discrimination against the elderly. Some positive ways the elderly are described: the elderly are valuable contributors to society, are held in high esteem, and have elevated statuses. Because of their life experiences, the elderly are able to contribute to such areas as human relations, management skills, sensitivity, and empathy. Studies show that older workers miss fewer workdays, have lower accident rates, and have a higher social standing. The elderly can teach young people coping and conflict resolution skills. The elderly vote in greater numbers than other age groups. Some negative ways the elderly are described: the elderly have diminished intellectual capacity, are senile, worthless, non-contributors with lower status, they lack technological skills, are frequently ill and non-productive; are unable to move quickly enough to avoid accidents. They have lower social standing and compete for jobs that the young need. They are unaware of contemporary political issues and are socially isolated.

22. Margaret Mead's findings illustrate gender roles that existed in preliterate societies in the 1930s. At that time, parallels between the societies she studied and industrial societies could be made. Generally women remained in the home and took care of the children, while men went to work. Gender roles have changed dramatically in the United States since 1935. During World War II, many women entered the workforce to replace men who went off to war. After the war, men regained workplace dominance. Since then, the number of women who work outside the home has increased dramatically. Many families today depend upon two salaries to meet expenses. Modern methods of birth control have allowed women to regulate the number and timing of their children. To a large extent this has freed women to pursue careers outside of the traditional ones, such as homemaker and caregiver for children. Some employers also provide child-care facilities for their employees. Recently, there has been a dramatic increase in the number of men who stay home to take care of children while the women in the family group work outside the home.

LESSON QUIZ 11-1

Matching

1. E	**2.** A	**3.** B	**4.** C	**5.** D

Multiple Choice

6. D	**7.** C	**8.** A	**9.** A	**10.** B

LESSON QUIZ 11-2

True/False

1. True
2. False
3. True
4. False
5. False

Multiple Choice

6. C **7.** B **8.** B **9.** D **10.** A

LESSON QUIZ 11-3

Completion

1. romantic love
2. long time
3. verbal and psychological abuse
4. declined
5. spousal abuse or child abuse

Multiple Choice

6. C **7.** B **8.** D **9.** A **10.** D

LESSON QUIZ 11-4

True/False

1. True
2. True
3. False
4. False
5. True

Multiple Choice

6. B **7.** A **8.** C **9.** A **10.** B

CHAPTER 11 TEST, FORM A

Matching

1. D **2.** H **3.** F **4.** E **5.** C
6. B **7.** G **8.** I **9.** A **10.** J

Multiple Choice

11. C **12.** B **13.** C **14.** A **15.** D
16. A **17.** C **18.** A **19.** B **20.** A

Essays

21. Answers will vary. Students can discuss the ways in which parents transmit values to their children as part of the process of socialization. In this family, part of the socialization process involves corporal punishment. In earlier times in this country, this method of dealing with children was more acceptable. Today's society views corporal punishment as a form of child abuse. Schools have a moral and legal responsibility to report suspected cases of child abuse to government authorities. Other possible responses can address the functionalist perspective of the family as a structure that has multiple benefits for individuals and society. In this particular example, Ms. Laureau suggests that the fear of school authorities has a great deal to do with Mrs.Yanelli's method of disciplining her son.

22. Some common features of an American family (although with the blending of many other cultures this may be somewhat different) are:

nuclear: a parent or parents and any children; may include a blended family; may include boomerang children

bilineal: inheritance is passed equally through both parents; lineage stems from both sides

egalitarian: decision making is shared equally

neolocal: couple lives apart from both sets of parents

monogamous: one husband with one wife at a time

23. Monogamy is the marriage between two people, usually a man and a woman at a time and is legal in all states. Several states now permit same-sex marriage. Polygamy is the marriage of a person to more than one person at a time and is not legal in the United States. Thus, monogamy and serial monogamy (having several spouses, but not at the same time) are the only accepted form of marriage in the United States today. In addition to laws preventing polygamy and polyandry, society frowns on these relationships and creates hardships on these families in terms of jail sentences, fines, exile, and diminished relations with others in the community.

CHAPTER 11 TEST, FORM B

Matching

1. I **2.** E **3.** H **4.** J **5.** B
6. C **7.** A **8.** D **9.** G **10.** F

Multiple Choice

11. D **12.** B **13.** D **14.** A **15.** C
16. C **17.** A **18.** D **19.** B **20.** C

Essays

21. The high rate for divorce and the relatively high rate of marriage in the late 1940s probably has a great deal to do with the end of World War II, and the changing roles of men and women that have occurred since then. The overall trend in the rates of both marriage and divorce is declining. Today, marriage is occurring at a later age in this country. The later age of marriage contributes to a lower divorce rate.

22. Answers will vary. Students may describe a traditional American wedding ceremony, or an American ceremony that has some rituals and traditions from other cultures.

LESSON QUIZ 12-1

True/False

1. False
2. False
3. True
4. True
5. False

Multiple Choice

6. C 7. A 8. A 9. A 10. D

LESSON QUIZ 12-2

Completion

1. provide day care for their children
2. abilities
3. growth or development
4. culture
5. keep up with their grade level

Multiple Choice

6. C 7. B 8. A 9. D 10. A

LESSON QUIZ 12-3

Matching

1. A 2. E 3. D 4. C 5. B

Multiple Choice

6. B 7. D 8. A 9. D 10. C

LESSON QUIZ 12-4

True/False

1. True
2. False
3. True
4. False
5. False

Multiple Choice

6. C 7. B 8. C 9. B 10. C

CHAPTER 12 TEST, FORM A

Matching

1. J 2. H 3. B 4. I 5. A
6. E 7. D 8. C 9. F 10. G

Multiple Choice

11. C 12. C 13. C 14. A 15. B
16. C 17. B 18. D 19. A 20. C

Essays

21. Charter schools are publicly funded schools that are operated like private schools by public school teachers and administrators. Magnet schools are public schools that attempt to achieve high standards by specializing in a certain area such as the performing arts or science. Private schools are privately/independently funded, have no governmental involvement, and often have a religious orientation. For-profit schools are supported by government funds but are run by private companies (i.e., Edison schools). Public schools are supported by public funds and are open to all who want to attend. The "best" school for an individual student would vary.

22. Answers will vary. Responses might focus on the way that teachers or textbooks socialize students. Students might also focus on the ways that the non-academic structure of their school is designed to foster values like cooperation, conformity, and competition.

23. Answers will vary. Horace Mann had no access to properly trained teachers. Thus, he was forced to educate himself. This experience contributed to Mann's desire for the state to provide education for its youth regardless of their economic status. In their answer, students should focus on the ways that education prepares people to function as active participants in civil and democratic social life. As the chapter makes clear, education in schools can be both academic and non-academic. Education also includes the transmission of important civic values such as cooperation, competition, and conformity.

CHAPTER 12 TEST, FORM B

Matching

1. F 2. E 3. J 4. D 5. G
6. H 7. C 8. B 9. I 10. A

Multiple Choice

11. B 12. B 13. D 14. C 15. C
16. A 17. B 18. B 19. B 20. C

Essays

21. Social institutions develop in order to meet society's basic needs. This is a functionalist's view. Schools teach the basic academic skills of reading, writing, and arithmetic, but they also transmit culture and they identify young talent. Schools also promote personal growth and development. The school is the driving force that unite students from a variety of ethnic backgrounds, races, and religions. Schools offer students opportunities for growth through many perspectives and experiences. For example, some schools encourage students to move outside the school and into the community to work with people who can direct them and expand their horizons both intellectually and emotionally. Schools must not only teach basic skills, but they also need to prepare young people for tomorrow's jobs in an ever-changing workplace. However, not all schools offer only positive experiences. Some are out-dated, some have below-standard facilities and lack contemporary curricula. Some schools lack community involvement such as providing day care centers for high school parents or medical care at the school site; some let certain students fall through the cracks when they need assistance such as special education, tutoring, or peer mediation. However, even the least effective school can improve if the community becomes involved.

22. "Or more" in the data shown for high school completion probably means "some college" was completed. In the college data, "or more" indicates some post graduate work was done. The high school rates for males and females show a steady, but not dramatic increase over the years shown in the graph. Male and female rates vary only slightly in the data for high school graduation. There is also a steady increase in college completion rates, but the data change from 1970 shows a dramatic change when compared to later years, especially for females. One likely explanation might be an increasing need for higher education to secure more technical jobs. Fewer job opportunities might now exist for high school graduates. Also, females might view additional appropriate roles apart from working in the home. Other answers are possible.

LESSON QUIZ 13-1

True/False

1. False
2. False
3. True
4. False
5. True

Multiple Choice

6. D 7. B 8. D 9. A 10. C

LESSON QUIZ 13-2

Completion

1. conflict perspective
2. television, or mass media
3. elitism
4. Accept any non-economic interest group, for example: League of Women Voters, Sierra Club, National Rifle Association, National Organization for Women, National Association for the Advancement of Colored People.
5. interest groups

Multiple Choice

6. B 7. D 8. D 9. A 10. C

LESSON QUIZ 13-3

True/False

1. True
2. True
3. False
4. False
5. True

Multiple Choice

6. A 7. A 8. D 9. A 10. B

LESSON QUIZ 13-4

True/False

1. True
2. False
3. True
4. False
5. False

Multiple Choice

6. A 7. D 8. A 9. C 10. B

LESSON QUIZ 13-5

Matching

1. C **2.** D **3.** E **4.** A **5.** B

Multiple Choice

6. D **7.** B **8.** A **9.** B **10.** C

CHAPTER 13 TEST, FORM A

Matching

1. H **2.** G **3.** I **4.** C **5.** B
6. D **7.** A **8.** J **9.** F **10.** E

Multiple Choice

11. C **12.** A **13.** A **14.** C **15.** A
16. A **17.** B **18.** B **19.** D **20.** A

Essays

21. Student answers may vary, but should be supported with information from the chapter. For example: It is not clear that democracy and civil liberties have been increasing during the past decade. Overall scores of countries for political and civil liberties have shown more countries declining than improving since 2005. While the percentage of free countries increased from 33 percent to 45 percent between 1981 and 2011, the percentage has remained essentially unchanged since 2001.

22. Responses regarding pros and cons may vary, but should be supported by information from the chapter. For example, students might cite limited liability and influence on government as pros, and limited control of daily operations and the minimal impact of voting for members of the board of directors as cons. Opinions regarding governmental regulations will vary, but opinions should be supported. For example, students might say they think corporations must be more strictly controlled to protect consumers. Likewise, they might state they think corporations will flourish and offer more jobs if they are less strictly controlled.

23. Responses will vary, but should be logical, clear, and strongly supported. For example, students might state that this category has typically involved intense physical labor, which in the past had been considered work for men. Women, however, have been entering these sectors of the workforce and can become extremely strong, so a gradual change (because these types of changes are historically gradual) in worker percentages is likely to occur.

CHAPTER 13 TEST, FORM B

Matching

1. F **2.** D **3.** G **4.** I **5.** A
6. C **7.** J **8.** B **9.** H **10.** E

Multiple Choice

11. C **12.** B **13.** A **14.** C **15.** C
16. B **17.** C **18.** D **19.** B **20.** B

Essays

21. Authoritarianism is a middle category between democracy and totalitarianism; however, it is closer to totalitarianism than to democracy. Authoritarianism is a political system controlled by elected or nonelected rulers who usually provide citizens with some degree of individual freedom. However, popular participation in government is not allowed. Totalitarianism lies at the opposite end of the political spectrum from democracy. A ruler with absolute power tries to control all aspects of a society. Students' reasons regarding government in the United States will differ, but should reflect the knowledge that people in the United States expect to have a voice in their government and to be represented by their elected officials.

22. Opinions may vary, but should be logical and strongly supported. For example, students might state that if a business has risen to the level of being able to create a monopoly, the business has earned this right, and its hard work should be rewarded. Alternatively, students might state that no business has the right to monopolize an industry as this gives the business the opportunity to take advantage of the consumer and others.

23. The only news sources available to voters in Jefferson's time were newspapers and journals. At that time, it took much longer for the "news" to be printed and distributed than it takes with today's 24 hour news cycle. In Jefferson's day people needed to be literate, or they would have had to have someone read to them. Today, news travels across the globe in seconds. People get most of their news from mass media such as television. It is an interesting commentary to realize that the survey identifies disinterest in learning about complicated issues. Jon Stewart's show is identified as a comedy show. But young people relate to his comedic touch on the news rather than the more serious approach favored by other news sources.

LESSON QUIZ 14-1

True/False

1. True
2. False
3. False
4. True
5. True

Multiple Choice

6. A	**7.** A	**8.** C	**9.** C	**10.** A

LESSON QUIZ 14-2

Completion

1. church
2. Amish
3. denominations
4. consequences or commitments
5. sect

Multiple Choice

6. B	**7.** C	**8.** A	**9.** D	**10.** A

LESSON QUIZ 14-3

True/False

1. True
2. False
3. True
4. False
5. False

Multiple Choice

6. D	**7.** B	**8.** A	**9.** C	**10.** A

CHAPTER 14 TEST, FORM A

Matching

1. H	**2.** G	**3.** J	**4.** F	**5.** A
6. C	**7.** I	**8.** E	**9.** D	**10.** B

Multiple Choice

11. A	**12.** C	**13.** D	**14.** D	**15.** A
16. A	**17.** D	**18.** D	**19.** C	**20.** B

Essays

21. The functionalist perspective looks at the contributions of religion to society. Conflict theory states that elites use religion to manipulate the masses—and the masses accept this control in the hope of a better existence in the afterlife. Symbolic interactionism states that people create symbolic meanings from their religious beliefs, rituals, and ideas to guide their everyday actions. Student opinions regarding the theoretical perspectives will vary, but should be strongly supported.
22. The five dimensions of religiosity are: belief, what a person considers to be true; ritual, a religious practice that the members of a religion are expected to perform; intellectual dimension, which may involve knowledge of holy or sacred texts or an interest in such religious aspects of human existence as evil, suffering, and death; experience, which encompasses certain feelings attached to religious expression; and consequences, which are the decisions and commitments people make as a result of religious beliefs, rituals, knowledge, or experiences. Students' opinions as to which is the most important may vary, but should be strongly supported. For example, students might state that ritual is the most important, as it shows how the person "lives" their religion.
23. Responses may vary. Students might state that this was true earlier during American history, but that many people in America no longer see themselves as "biblical," but instead view their existence as strongly tied to governmental, political, and economic influences. This feeling helps contribute to the secularization of American society. Other students might feel that because society has strayed so far from "religious" beliefs that we should return to religion to guide our everyday lives.

CHAPTER 14 TEST, FORM B

Matching

1. I	**2.** F	**3.** G	**4.** B	**5.** H
6. C	**7.** A	**8.** D	**9.** J	**10.** E

Multiple Choice

11. D	**12.** B	**13.** C	**14.** A	**15.** D
16. D	**17.** C	**18.** A	**19.** C	**20.** B

Essays

21. Examples will vary, but should be accurate and logical. For example, students might reference the following: some Bolivian tin miners attach sacred meaning to figures of the devil and of bulls and others do not. So these items that are sacred to some of the tin miners are profane to those who hold other beliefs and practice other customs. Students' opinions will vary, but should be logical and strongly supported. Students will likely state that this does make sense, as cultures have developed at different times and places throughout history.
22. Responses may vary, but should be logical and strongly supported. For example, students might state that it is important for sociologists to be objective because their function is to observe and report on society—and the results of their studies can be applied to many important situations. Opinions regarding whether a sociologist can actually be objective and refrain from interjecting personal beliefs based on faith into research will vary, but should be strongly supported.
23. Response may vary. A positive force can be the promotion of a sense of belonging. People can share ideas, ways of life, and ethnic identity with others of similar beliefs. A negative effect might occur when the dominant religious group oppresses a religious minority in the country. Some people might resort to violence to make their religion more powerful and to empower themselves. Other examples of negative religious actions can often be seen in mass media reports.

LESSON QUIZ 15-1

Matching

1. B **2.** D **3.** A **4.** E **5.** C

Multiple Choice

6. A **7.** C **8.** D **9.** D **10.** B

LESSON QUIZ 15-2

True/False

1. False
2. False
3. True
4. True
5. True

Multiple Choice

6. A **7.** C **8.** A **9.** B **10.** C

LESSON QUIZ 15-3

Completion

1. city
2. Industrial Revolution
3. urban growth
4. central-city dilemma
5. agricultural revolution

Multiple Choice

6. A **7.** C **8.** A **9.** D **10.** A

LESSON QUIZ 15-4

True/False

1. False
2. False
3. True
4. False
5. False

Multiple Choice

6. D **7.** A **8.** D **9.** B **10.** B

CHAPTER 15 TEST, FORM A

Matching

1. E **2.** D **3.** I **4.** H **5.** G
6. B **7.** A **8.** J **9.** F **10.** C

Multiple Choice

11. A **12.** C **13.** C **14.** A **15.** D
16. C **17.** B **18.** D **19.** A **20.** A

Essays

21. Gross migration rate is the number of persons per 1,000 members of a population who enter or leave a geographic area. Net migration rate is the annual increase or decrease per 1,000 members of a population resulting from migration into and out of the population. Rural-to-urban migration occurs when people move from rural to urban areas. Urban-to-rural migration occurs when people move from urban to rural areas. Students' opinions regarding the year 2025 may differ, but should be strongly supported by information from the chapter.

22. The factors are: size, the number of people; distribution, how and where people are located; compositions, what groups make up the population; and age structure, the ages represented in the population. The processes are: fertility, birth; mortality, death; and migration, movement from one place to another. Students' opinions regarding which two are the most important may vary, but should be logical and strongly supported by content from the chapter.

23. The urban housing development is a relatively recent phenomenon because the urban setting from which it grows is relatively recent. Responses regarding reasons for the power of the example may vary. The article states that the projects were built to isolate poor people from the dominant society. In effect, projects are a kind of vertical urban "ghetto." Students might state that the quote shows the desperation that existed in people who lived in the project.

CHAPTER 15 TEST, FORM B

Matching

1. C	2. J	3. E	4. A	5. H
6. G	7. B	8. I	9. F	10. D

Multiple Choice

11. C	12. A	13. A	14. B	15. B
16. C	17. B	18. B	19. A	20. D

Essays

21. The infant mortality rate is the number of deaths among infants younger than one year of age per 1,000 live births. It is considered a good indicator of the health status of a group because infants are the first to suffer from a lack of good medical care and poor sanitation. Students' opinions regarding other indicators may vary, but should be logical and strongly supported.

22. Although the population of New York-Newark has increased, it is no longer the largest urban area shown in the graphs. The population of Tokyo has surpassed that of New York-Newark. You might infer that the birth rate has increased, and the mortality rate has decreased in the cities shown. Further research might also support the belief that there might have been an increase in the migration rate to urban areas in some cities. There might also have been a decrease in migration rates to rural areas in some of the cities shown. These factors, and others, would contribute to the increase of the populations of cities shown in the graphs.

23. Responses may vary. Malthus thought that factors that increased mortality—for example, famine, disease, and war—would act to limit population growth. Decreasing fertility and marrying later in life would also act to limit population growth. He also stressed that education would encourage people to have smaller families. Many of the checks that Malthus described were undoubtedly effective at limiting population growth, but mostly by producing an increased rate of mortality. Today, people, with proper education, are often able to choose appropriate methods to limit family size.

LESSON QUIZ 16-1

Completion

1. behaviors
2. remain the same
3. process
4. demographers
5. revolution

Multiple Choice

6. D	7. A	8. B	9. A	10. D

LESSON QUIZ 16-2

Modified True/False

1. FALSE—Change is one of the most CONSTANT features of American society.
2. FALSE— CONFLICT THEORY draws the conclusion that enactment of civil rights laws in the 1960s was a result of the struggle related to racial equality.
3. TRUE
4. TRUE
5. FALSE— SYMBOLIC INTERACTIONISM identifies decreasing shared values as a source of social insecurity.

Multiple Choice

6. B	7. C	8. A	9. D	10. B

LESSON QUIZ 16-3

Modified True/False

1. TRUE
2. FALSE—Fashion is a way of dressing or behaving that is widely accepted, BUT CONTINUALLY CHANGING.
3. FALSE—Planking and streaking are examples of FADS.
4. FALSE— Contagion theory focuses on the spread of EMOTION in a crowd.
5. TRUE

Multiple Choice

6. D **7.** C **8.** D **9.** A **10.** A

LESSON QUIZ 16-4

Completion

1. value-added theory
2. resource-mobilization theory
3. strain or structural strain
4. precipitating factor
5. alternative

Multiple Choice

6. A **7.** C **8.** C **9.** B **10.** D

CHAPTER 16 TEST, FORM A

Matching

1. H **2.** I **3.** E **4.** J **5.** C
6. B **7.** G **8.** D **9.** A **10.** F

Multiple Choice

11. B **12.** D **13.** B **14.** C **15.** A
16. D **17.** D **18.** B **19.** C **20.** D

Essays

21. Contagion theory states that members of crowds stimulate each other to higher and higher levels of emotion and irrational behavior. Emergent-norm theory states that norms develop to guide crowd behavior. Convergence theory states that crowds are formed by people who deliberately congregate with like-minded others. Students' examples and opinions may vary, but should be clear, logical, and strongly supported by chapter content.
22. A revolutionary movement, such as the American Revolution, attempts to change the total structure of society. A reformative movement, such as the Woman's Christian Temperance Union, aims to effect more limited changes in a society. A redemptive movement, such as Alcoholics Anonymous, focuses on making a radical change within individuals. An alternative movement, such as Zero Population Growth/Population Connection, is focused on bringing about limited changes in individuals. While examples are included above, student examples may differ. Student statements regarding a new movement may vary, but should be clear, logical, and strongly supported by chapter content.
23. Each stage adds its value to the final cost of the finished product. The key element is that the earlier stages must combine according to a certain pattern before the next stage can contribute its particular value to the finished product. In the case of making an automobile each step must 'wait' for completion of the earlier processes. Smelser thought that every stage in the process is a necessary condition for the appropriate and effective addition of value in the next step. The value-added theory used to explain economic trends is also applied to social movements. Each step in the process is necessary in order for the next step to proceed. Opinions regarding reasons for development and addition or deletion of conditions may vary, but should be clear, logical, and strongly supported by chapter content.

CHAPTER 16 TEST, FORM B

Matching

1. D **2.** J **3.** H **4.** B **5.** F
6. A **7.** E **8.** I **9.** G **10.** C

Multiple Choice

11. A **12.** A **13.** C **14.** B **15.** C
16. B **17.** B **18.** D **19.** A **20.** C

Essays

21. The value-added theory holds that certain conditions must exist for social movements to occur; resource-mobilization theory focuses on the process through which members of a social movement secure and use the resources needed to advance their cause. Student discussions, examples, and opinions regarding the likely changes may vary, but should be supported by content from the chapter.

22. Globalization is the development of an increasingly integrated global economy. During recent decades, globalization has been an agent of diffusion. More broadly, it is a process that also results in increasingly integrated political, cultural, and environmental system. As the world becomes more integrated, individual societies can experience great change. Student examples may vary, but are likely to include the following: globalization resulting in the rise of obesity throughout the world, the opening of global markets bringing down the price of food, the spread of technology changing the nature of work for many. Student opinions regarding the future may vary, but are likely to state that globalization will continue to be an agent of diffusion. Student opinions should be clear, logical, and strongly supported by content from the chapter.

23. It illustrates the value-added theory. The graphic illustrates the steps in the value-added theory. The arrow-shaped sections show in a graphic form that one step precedes the other and the shape of the sections implies that an earlier step leads to the step directly above it. This prior step must occur before the next step can occur.